Also by Peter Haining

HOLE IN FUN
A Round of Humorous Golfing Stories

HOOK, LINE AND LAUGHTER

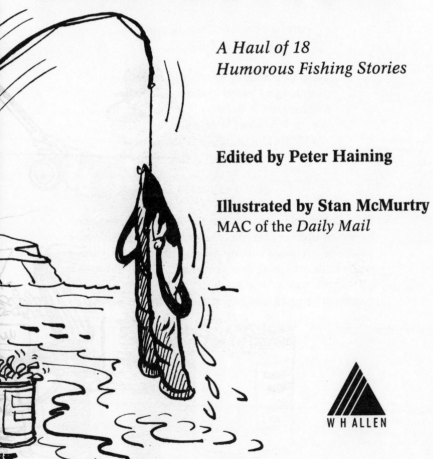

*A Haul of 18
Humorous Fishing Stories*

Edited by Peter Haining

Illustrated by Stan McMurtry
MAC of the *Daily Mail*

W H ALLEN

First published in Great Britain by
W.H. Allen & Co. Plc

Set in Concorde by Phoenix Photosetting
Printed and bound in Great Britain by
Mackays of Chatham PLC, Chatham, Kent
for the Publishers W.H. Allen & Co. Plc
Sekforde House, 175/9 St John Street,
London EC1V 4LL

ISBN 0 491 03439 3

For
LOU WILKES
In memory of all those that
got away in the Ardeche

'Fishing is a rod and a line, with a fly at one end
and a fool at the other.'

SAMUEL JOHNSON

On Fly Fishing

CONTENTS

CONTENTS

Some years ago when I was researching a book about humorous tombstone epitaphs I came across this amusing instance in an Essex graveyard. (I'll spare the fisherman's relatives their blushes by not revealing either his name or the exact location of the grave.)

> 'He angled in the sparkling brook
> With all an angler's skill;
> He lied about the fish he took,
> And here he's lying still.'

For those to whom angling is something akin to a religion such a remark about their sport may seem little short of slanderous. But there can be no doubt that fishing has attracted as much fun and ridicule over the years as any sport. Perhaps more than some because, of course, of the ancient tradition of exaggerating the truth about a catch – or, alternatively, the lack of it!

Although increasing the size of a fish or adding a little to its weight is probably the extent of most angler's little white lies, others have gone to extraordinary lengths to ensure success in the sport. In a fishing contest as recently as 1987, for example, four fishermen secretly slipped into the water some fish they had caught the previous day and then rehooked them to carry off the prizes!

Where size is concerned, the stories fishermen tell are almost endless, though the one that always makes me smile features a man who claimed to have hooked a fish so big that it dragged him out of the boat.

'I suppose you got a nasty soaking?' his listener apparently said with a smile.

'Not at all,' came the indignant reply. 'I fell on the fish!'

There are just as many funny stories about incidents which have occurred to fishermen while they have been waiting patiently for a catch. Take the one about a young lady angler competing in a contest who was finally unable to resist the call of nature.

Almost at bursting point, she left her rod and line and slipped away to a nearby public convenience, where for her relief she was well and truly grateful. When she returned to the river bank, however, she found to her dismay that she had been disqualified. And the official who had disqualified her was . . . her own father!

The attraction of fishing can appeal to even the very young, and whenever I see small boys or girls around a pond I am reminded of the story of the schoolchild who was asked to make up a sentence containing the word, 'amphibious'. His answer was a gem: 'Most fish stories am fibious.'

My own interest in the funny side of fishing I can trace back to my days as a journalist and an interview I once conducted with that ebullient jazz singer, George Melly. A man of sparkling good humour, who tells jokes as easily and entertainingly as he sings, I remember being somewhat taken aback when I asked him what his hobbies were.

'Trout fishing,' he said without a moment's pause. 'Put me in the middle of a stream with a rod in my hand and I'm perfectly content.'

I looked hard at that mischievous face to see if he was pulling my leg. I could imagine George doing almost anything but standing waist deep in freezing cold water for hours on end. He obviously read my thoughts.

'It's no joke,' he insisted. 'Fishing is the complete opposite to what I do for a living so it really relaxes me.'

So it transpired that I duly noted in my report how George Melly, jazz singer extraordinaire, spent his spare time. But, somehow, the memory of his comment would not go away. As a result, over the years I've always been interested in the funny side of fishing – in particular comic short stories about angling. And not altogether to my surprise I have learned that it is a far from modern tradition.

Turning back the pages of literature, it is possible to find no less a person than the great bard himself, William Shakespeare, having a little fun at the expense of fishermen in his play, *Antony and Cleopatra*:

> 'Twas merry when
> You wager'd on your angling, when your diver
> Did hang a salt-fish on his hook, which he
> With fervency drew up.'

Another anonymous scribe not so long afterwards revealed a similar penchant for humour when he penned the following definition of a fisherman: 'He riseth up early in the morning and disturbeth the whole household. Mighty are his preparations. He goeth forth full of hope. When the day is far spent, he returneth, smelling of strong drink, and the truth is not in him.'

There is even humour to be found in the very first classic book on fishing, *The Compleat Angler*, written by Izaak Walton in 1653, which has the distinction of being the most reprinted book in the English language, with the exception of *The Bible* and *The Book of Common Prayer*. Let me offer just two instances to demonstrate what I mean.

Take this extract in which Walton compares a trout with a *crocodile* – a creature few of his seventeenth-century readers were familiar with let alone had seen!

'The Trout,' he writes, 'is of a more sudden growth than other fish: concerning which you are to take notice that he lives not so long as the Perch and divers other fishes do. And next you are to take notice that he is not like the Crocodile, which if he

[11]

lives never so long, yet always thrives till his death. But tis not so with the Trout, for after he is come to his full growth, he declines in his body and keeps his bigness or thrives only in his head till his death.'

Or how about this story of a pike caught by *a mule* . . .

'All Pike that live long prove changeable to their keepers, because their life is maintained by the death of so many other fish, even those of their own kind; which has made him by some writers to be called the tyrant of the rivers, or the fresh water wolf, by reason of his bold, greedy, devouring disposition; which is so keen, as Gesner relates, a man going to a pond (where it seems a Pike had devoured all the fish) to water his mule, had a Pike bit his mule by the lips; to which the Pike hung so fast, that the mule drew him out of the water; and by that accident the owner of the mule angled out the Pike!'

In an amusing footnote to these comments, Izaak Walton insists that they are true having been told to him by 'persons of credit.' He adds, 'And I shall conclude these observations by telling you what a man has observed, "It is a hard thing to persuade the belly because it has no ears!"'

Despite these early examples of fishing humour – and there are numerous others I could cite – this collection actually begins with the work of the first writer to specialise in comic short stories about fishing, the Scotsman, Christopher North, who began to write them about 150 years ago. From his inspiration, a whole body of similar humour has developed and continued to this day – the best examples of which are to be found in the pages which follow.

One of the great features about angling, of course, is that it appeals to people in all walks of life and is accessible to everyone. Indeed, in Britain, fishing is the nation's leading participant sport, with upwards of three million people regularly casting their lines into our waters. And among their number are such well-known people as the Prince of Wales, singer Roger Daltry, actor Sir Michael Hordern, actress Diana Rigg, and football manager, Jack Charlton.

All have instances of fishing humour to relate, but my favourite 'tall story' is one that the late American singer, Bing Crosby, a life-long enthusiast of the sport, told some years back. I repeat it in his own words.

'One day,' said Bing, 'I went fishing with my brother and, though he caught a limit of trout, I fished right next to him without a bite. The next day we hit the same hole, and again he got a creelful in no time at all, and I was blanked. On the third day, I sneaked out without my brother and fished in the hole my brother had so much success in.

'Nothing happened all day, and as I was packing up to leave a big trout stuck his head a foot out of the water and said, "Where's your brother today?"'

Though for the true angler there is no substitute for actually going fishing, if circumstances intrude he may find in the pages which follow some amusement and even the odd moment of nostalgia! So welcome, then, to the world of hook, line and laughter – perhaps most neatly expressed in the opening line of an essay written a few years ago by a small boy on the subject of fish.

'The biggest part of a fish,' he began with a flourish, 'is the tale.'

PETER HAINING,
Boxford, Suffolk.
January 1989.

1

TWADDLE ON TWEEDSIDE

by Christopher North

THE oldest funny story about fishing is probably a variation
on the tale of 'the one that got away', but the actual tradition of
writing humorous short stories about the sport can be traced
back to the early years of the nineteenth century and the witty
pen of a Scottish professor, John Wilson, who wrote under the
pen-name of Christopher North. Wilson was one of the first
and most prolific contributors to the now famous Edinburgh-
based publication, *Blackwood's Magazine*, following its
establishment in 1817, and his comic stories, quite a number
about angling, have been credited with playing a major part in
the success of the journal, which still thrives to this day.

Wilson was born in Paisley and first discovered the joys of
angling under the tutelage of his father in the local rivers and
burns. Following his education in Glasgow and at Oxford
University – where he revealed a formidable intellect as well
as considerable talent as an athlete and sportsman – he lived
for a while beside Lake Windermere and became friendly with
some of the famous literary figures of the day including
Wordsworth, Southey, Coleridge and De Quincey. In 1815,
he returned to Scotland where he settled in Edinburgh and
briefly worked as a lawyer. But writing was what gave him the
greatest satisfaction while sport was his passion, and soon he
was combining both in journalistic essays to make a successful career.

Among his contemporaries in Scotland at this time were
three great anglers, James Hogg, Thomas Tod Stoddart and

William Scrope, and it was in their company that he fished many of the fine rivers of the North. Wilson, though, never allowed angling to become an obsession with him, and he took delight in making spirited fun of those who did. Every so often, the pages of *Blackwood's Magazine* would be enlivened by a contribution from him which touched on some funny element of fishing or else an incident in which he had been involved. When Wilson was elected to be Professor of Moral Philosophy at Edinburgh University, he began collecting his magazine contributions together into books which proved very popular with readers all over Britain. His items on fishing are to be found in such volumes as *Noctes Ambrosianae* (1822–35), *Anglimania* (1833) and *The Recreations of Christopher North* (1855–8), and these earned him nicknames from his readers such as 'M.A.' – 'Master of Angling' – and 'F.R.S.' – 'Fisherman Royal of Scotland'!

One of the professor's favourite fishing haunts was along the banks of the beautiful River Tweed, and it was on an angling expedition there in the early 1830s that the events occurred which inspired this first story. The problem that confronts the narrator is one that any fisherman might experience – though the outcome is certainly unexpected!

TWADDLE ON TWEEDSIDE

Angling, in boyhood, youth, and manhood's prime, was with us a passion. Now it is an affection. The first glimpse of the water, caught at a distance, used to set our hearts a-beating, and 'Without stop or stay down the rocky way' we rushed to the pastime.

If we saw a villain with a creel on his back, wading waist-deep, and from the middle of the stream commanding every cranny in among the tree roots on both sides – in spite of copse or timber – we cursed and could almost have killed him; and how we guffawed when such a reprobate, at a chance time

losing his footing among the coggly and sliddery stones, with
many staggers, fell sprawling first back and then forwards, and
finally, half-choked and grievously incommoded by the belt of
his emptied basket coiling round his thrapple, while the dead
trouts were seen floating about with their yellow bellies, went
hatless down the current, and came sneaking out at the ford
like a half-drowned rat – pity that the vagabond had not gone
over the waterfall – a better death than his father's, who, it was
well known, was hanged for sheep-stealing at Carlisle!

Now we can look carelessly at a whole regiment of
leathern-aprons, all at once in single file poaching the Tweed
the whole way from Peebles to Innerleithen. Nothing that
may happen in this world now would make us lose our temper. With the utmost equanimity we can now look up to our
tailfly – both bobbers – and several yards of line, inextricably
hanked, high up a tree; or on the whole concern by a sudden
jerk converted into an extraordinary hair-ball, such as one
reads of being found in the stomachs of cows. The sudden
breaking of our top just at the joint, which is left full of rotten
wood – no knife in our pocket and no spare top in our butt – a
calamity which has caused frequent suicides – from us elicits
but a philosophical smile at the Vanity of Human Wishes.

Here's as pretty a piece of workmanship as the rod maker
Phin ever put out of hand – light as cork, and true as steel –
and such a run! Now, let us choose an irresistible leash of
insects – and we lay a sovereign to a sixpence that we are fast
in silver scales before half-a-dozen throws. Where the deuce is
our tackle-book? Not in this pocket – nor this – nor this – nor
this. Confound it – that is very odd – it can't surely be in our
breeches – no – no – not there – curse it – that is very queer –
nor in the crown of our hat – no – dang it – that is enough to try
the patience of a saint! Where the devil can it be? Not in our
basket – no—and Tommy! can we, like an infernal idiot, have
left our book on the breakfast table back at Clovenford?

O the born idiots of the Inn! Not to see our book lying on
the breakfast table. The blind blockheads must have taken it

[18]

for the family Bible. And Helen, too! not to see and send it after us! Never again, were we to drag on a miserable existence like Methusaleh's, will we have the wretched folly to come out to Clovenford! From this blasted hour we swear to give up angling for ever – and we have a mind to break into twenty thousand pieces this great, big, thick, coarse, clumsy, useless and lumbering rod!

We beseech us to look at *that – the take – the take is on –* by all that is prolific, the surface of the water is crawling with noses and back-fins – scores of pounders are plumping about in all directions – and oh, Gemini! the ripple over by yonder, in the shallow water of that little greensward-bottomed bay, betrays a monster. Such a day, and such an hour, and such a minute for certain slaughter – for bloody sport – never saw we with our eyes – though we have for fifty years and more been an angler. People in pulpits preach patience – blockheads in black and with bands – smooth and smug smiling sinners who never knew disappointment nor despair – nor have the souls of the poor prigs capacity to conceive such a trial as this. There they go – heads and tails – leap-leap-leaping – but no splash – for the largest dip noiselessly as the least – and we hear only a murmur. – Oh lord!

Why are not people planting potatoes somewhere in sight? Nobody dibbling in the garden. Door of the house locked – but we might walk into the byre. The fools have gone to the fair! We are deafened by eternal talk about education in Scotland – why then is there not here a school – that we might get a boy to run to Clovenford for our book? It seems especially absurd for the county to have put itself to great expense in making a turnpike road through such an uninhabited district as this. Not a soul to be seen far as the eye can reach – nothing in the live way but sheep and rooks – and they do bleat and caw, it must be confessed, to an odious degree, and in a most disgusting manner. As to going back all the way, two Scotch – but many English miles – to Clovenford for our book – and then coming back to begin fishing about the middle of the day

– when it is well known that it often unaccountably happens you may then as well angle in the Tweed for oysters – that would be madness; yet staying here without tackle is folly; and in such a dilemma, what the devil – we say again – is to be done? But who is this suddenly arrived?

Heaven bless thy bright face, thou golden-headed girl! whence comest thou into this nook of earth – yes – from Fairyland. What? Herding cows? Well – well – child! don't be frightened – you have overheard us talking to ourselves – and perhaps think us "the strange Gentleman"; but it was a mere soliloquy – so see – here's half-a-crown – run you to Clovenford and ask Helen for our book – our tackle-book – and you shall have another on your return – provided you are back within the hour. Never mind about the cows. We will look after them – CHRISTOPHER NORTH IN THE CHARACTER OF COWHERD – what a subject for our dear Wullie Allan! Yet, did not Apollo for nine years guard the flocks of Admetus?

Why, 'tis but nine now. Time enough from ten to six to crowd our creel, till the lid fly open. Many a man would have been much discomposed on such an occasion as this; but thanks to a fine natural temper, and to a philosophic and religious education, we have kept ourselves cool as a cucumber. This forgetfulness of ours is likely to prove a lucky accident after all, for hitherto there has been hardly a breath stirring, and we did not much like that glimmer on the water. True, a few fins were visible – but they were merely playing, and we question if a single snout would have taken the fly. But now the air is beginning to circulate, and to go rustling up among the thick-budded, and here and there almost leafy trees, in little delightful whirlwinds. The sun is sobered in the mild sky by the gentle obscuration of small soft rainy or rather dewy-looking clouds; one feels the inexpressible difference between heat and warmth, in this genial temperature; and what could have been the matter with our eyes that they were blind, or with our soul that it was insensible, to that prodigal profusion of primroses embedding the banks and braes with

beauty, in good time to be succeeded by the yet brighter
broom!

Shall we take a swim? The cow-herdess might surprise us in
the pool, and swoon with fear at sight of the water-kelpie!

> A dream of old, born of that sudden smile
> Of watery sunshine, comes across our brain.

Twenty years ago, at two o'clock of a summer morning we left
the schoolhouse at Dalmally, where we were lodging, and
walked up Glenorchy – fourteen miles long – to Inveruren.
On the banks of that fishy loch we stood, eyeing the sunshine
beautifully warming the breezy dark moss-water. We un-
screwed the brass head of our walking cane, to convert it into
a rod; when, lo! the hollow was full of emptiness! We had
disembowelled it the evening before, and left all the pieces on
the chest of drawers in our bedroom! This was as bad as being
without our book. The dizziness in our head was as if the earth
had dwindled down to the size of the mere spot on which we
stood, but still kept moving as before at the same rate, on its
own axis, and round the sun. On recovering our stationary
equilibrium, we put our pocket pistol to our head, and blew
out its brains into our mouth – in the liquid character of
Glenlivet. Then down the glen we bounded like a deer belling
in his season, and by half past seven were in the schoolhouse.
We said nothing – not that we were either sullen or sulky; but
stern resolution compressed out lips, which opened but to
swallow a few small loaves and fishes – and having performed
twenty-eight miles, we started again for the Loch. At eleven –
for we took our swing easily and steadily – our five flies were
on the water. By sunset we had killed twenty dozen – none
above a pound – and by far the greater number about a quarter
– but the *tout-ensemble* was imposing – and the weight could
not have been short of five stone. We filled both creels (one
used for salmon), bag, and pillowslip, and all the pockets
about our person – and at first peep of the evening star went
our ways again down the glen towards Dalmally. We reached

the schoolhouse 'ae wee short hour ayont the twal,' having been on our legs almost all the four-and-twenty hours, and for eight up to the waist in water – distance walked, fifty-six miles – trouts killed, twenty dozen and odds – and weight carried.

> At the close of the day when the hamlet was still,
> And mortals the sweets of forgetfulness proved,

certainly seventy pounds for fourteen miles; and if the tale be not true, may Mayday miss Maga.

And, now, alas! we could not hobble for our book from the holms of Ashiestiel to Clovenford!

But here comes Iris, with our book in her bosom. She espies us, and holding it up above 'her beautiful and shining golden head,' it seems to our ears as if the kind creature were singing a song.

Now, Mary – we knew your name was Mary, the moment we saw you – Mary Riddle – we ken you sing – sae gie's a sang, my bonny bit wee winsome lassie – while we are rummaging our book. But what's the matter? What's the matter?

'O sir,' she says, 'you've no been leukin after the kye – for, mercy me! there's three o' the twa-year-auld Hielant nowt gotten into the garden. O Sir! you're a bad herd!'

2

A SHARK STORY

by Thomas Chandler Haliburton

T. C. HALIBURTON has been described as the 'Founder of American Humour' and certainly his character Sam Slick whose hilarious exploits and unlikely adventures first appeared in US newspapers was a forerunner of many similar figures of fun. Sam was not unlike Charles Dickens' great character from *Pickwick Papers*, Sam Weller, and the stories about him were later collected in volumes such as *The Clockmaker: or, Sayings and Doings of Samuel Slick of Slickville* (1837) and *The Attaché: or, Sam Slick in England* (1843). Like his creator, Sam loved fishing and both books feature the sport in various short episodes.

Thomas Haliburton was born in Windsor, Nova Scotia, and followed a not dissimilar path to his Scottish contemporary, John Wilson, by first working in the law and then serving in the House of Assembly where he also began writing. His ideal method of relaxation was sea fishing in the fine waters around North America – especially on the trail of sharks – and not surprisingly his hobby found its way into his stories. Like Wilson, Haliburton had a strong sense of humour, and his facility as a satirist soon made him popular with readers all over America. The stories of Sam Slick sealed his reputation; while *Traits of American Humour* (1852) made him internationally famous.

In 1856, Haliburton crossed the Atlantic to live in Britain, settling at Launceston in Cornwall, not that far from some fine sea fishing spots around the coast of the West Country which he often frequented looking for sport. From 1859–63 he put his knowledge of administration to good use as the MP for Launceston, and then following his retirement spent his last days angling on the more peaceful local rivers.

Though, as I mentioned, Sam Slick was an occasional angler, I have not selected an item about him for this anthology as the books in which he appeared can still be found. Instead, I have picked a story written in 1852 in which Haliburton has utilised his knowledge of shark fishing in America. What follows is certainly a fisherman's 'Tall Story' – and there are few better to be found!

A SHARK STORY

'Well, gentlemen, I'll go ahead, if you say so. Here's the story. It is true, upon my honour, from beginning to end – every word of it. I once crossed over to Faulkner's island to fish for *tautaugs*, as the north-side people call black fish, on the reefs hard by, in the Long Island Sound. Tim Titus (who died of the dropsy down at Shinnecock point, last spring) lived there then. Tim was a right good fellow, only he drank rather too much.

'It was during the latter part of July; the sharks and the dog-fish had just begun to spoil sport. When Tim told me about the sharks, I resolved to go prepared to entertain these aquatic savages with all becoming attention and regard, if there should chance to be any interloping about our fishing ground. So, we rigged out a set of extra large hooks, and shipped some rope-yarn and steel chain, an axe, a couple of

[25]

clubs, and an old harpoon, in addition to our ordinary equipments, and off we started. We threw out our anchor at half ebb tide, and took some thumping large fish; two of them weighed thirteen pounds – so you may judge. The reef where we lay was about half a mile from the island, and, perhaps, a mile from the Connecticut shore. We floated there, very quietly, throwing out and hauling in, until the breaking of my line, with a sudden and severe jerk, informed me that the sea attorneys were in waiting, down stairs; and we accordingly prepared to give them a retainer. A salt pork cloak upon one of our magnum hooks forthwith engaged one of the gentlemen in our service. We got him alongside, and by dint of piercing, and thrusting, and banging, we accomplished a most exciting and merry murder. We had business enough of the kind to keep us employed until near low water. By this time, the sharks had all cleared out, and the black fish were biting again; the rock began to make its appearance above the water, and in a little while its hard bald head was entirely dry. Tim now proposed to set me out upon the rock, while he rowed ashore to get the jug, which, strange to say, we had left at the house. I assented to this proposition; first, because I began to feel the effects of the sun upon my tongue, and needed something to take, by the way of medicine; and secondly because the rock was a favourite spot for rod and reel, and famous for luck: so I took my *traps*, and a box of bait, and jumped upon my new station. Tim made for the island.

'Not many men would willingly have been left upon a little barren reef that was covered by every flow of the tide, in the midst of a waste of waters, at such a distance from the shore, even with an assurance from a companion more to be depended upon than mine, that he would return immediately and take him off. But some how or other, the excitement of the sport was so high, and the romance of the situation was so delightful, that I thought of nothing else but the prospect of my fun, and the contemplation of the novelty and beauty of the scene. It was a mild, pleasant afternoon, in harvest time.

The sky was clear and pure. The deep blue sound, heaving all around me, was studded with craft of all descriptions and dimensions, from the dipping sail-boat to the rolling mer-chantman, sinking and rising like sea-birds sporting with their white wings in the surge. The grain and grass on the neigh-bouring farms were gold and green, and gracefully they bent obeisance to a gently breathing southwester. Farther off, the high upland, and the distant coast, gave a dim relief to the prominent features of the landscape, and seemed the rich but dusky frame of a brilliant fairy picture. Then, how still it was! Not a sound could be heard, except the occasional rustling of my own motion, and the water beating against the sides, or gurgling in the fissures of the rock, or except now and then the cry of a solitary saucy gull, who would come out of his way in the firmament, to see what I was doing without a boat, all alone, in the middle of the sound; and who would hover, and cry, and chatter, and make two or three circling swoops and dashes at me, and then, after having satisfied his curiosity, glide away in search of some other food to scream at.

'I soon became half indolent, and quite indifferent about fishing; so I stretched myself out at full length upon the rock and gave myself up to the luxury of looking and thinking. The divine exercise soon put me fast asleep. I dreamed away a couple of hours, and longer might have dreamed, but for a tired fish-hawk who chose to make my head his resting place, and who waked and started me to my feet.

'"Where is Tim Titus?" I muttered to myself, as I strained my eyes over the now darkened water. But none was near me to answer that interesting question, and nothing was to be seen of either Tim or his boat. "He should have been here long ere this," thought I, "and he promised faithfully not to stay long – could he have forgotten? or has he paid too much devotion to the jug?"

'I began to feel uneasy, for the tide was rising fast, and soon would cover the top of the rock, and high water mark was at least a foot above my head. I buttoned up my coat, for either

the coming coolness of the evening, or else my growing appre-
hensions, had set me trembling and chattering most painfully.
I braced my nerves, and set my teeth, and tried to hum
"Begone, dull care," keeping time with my fists upon my
thighs. But what music! What melancholy merriment! I
started and shuddered at the doleful sound of my own voice. I
am not naturally a coward; but I should like to know the man
who would not, in such a situation, be alarmed. It is a cruel
death to die to be merely drowned, and to go through the
ordinary commonplaces of suffocation; but to see your death
gradually rising to your eyes, to feel the water rising, inch by
inch, upon your shivering sides, and to anticipate the certainly
coming, choking struggle for your last breath, when, with the
gurgling sound of an overflowing brook taking a new direction, the cold brine pours into mouth, ears, and nostrils,
usurping the seat and avenues of health and life, and, with
gradual flow, stifling – smothering – suffocating! It were better
to die a thousand common deaths.

'This is one of the instances in which, it must be admitted,
salt water is not a pleasant subject of contemplation. However, the rock was not yet covered, and hope, blessed hope,
stuck faithfully by me. To beguile, if possible, the weary time, I
put on a bait, and threw out for fish. I was sooner successful
than I could have wished to be, for hardly had my line struck
the water, before the hook was swallowed, and my rod was
bent with the dead hard pull of a twelve foot shark. I let him
run about fifty yards, and then reeled up. He appeared not at
all alarmed, and I could scarcely feel him bear upon my fine
hair line. He followed the pull gently and unresisting, came up
to the rock, laid his nose upon its side, and looked up into my
face, not as if utterly unconcerned, but with a sort of quizzical
impudence, as though he perfectly understood the precarious
nature of my situation. The conduct of my captive renewed
and increased my alarm. And well it might; for the tide was
now running over a corner of the rock behind me, and a small
stream rushed through a cleft, or fissure, by my side, and

formed a puddle at my very feet. I broke my hook out of the monster's mouth, and leaned upon my rod for support.

'"Where is Tim Titus?" I cried aloud. "Curse on the drunken vagabond! Will he never come?"

'My ejaculations did no good. No Timothy appeared. It became evident that I must prepare for drowning, or for action. The reef was completely covered, and the water was above the soles of my feet. I was not much of a swimmer, and as to ever reaching the island, I could not even hope for that. However, there was no alternative, and I tried to encourage myself, by reflecting that necessity was the mother of invention, and that desperation will sometimes ensure success. Besides, too, I considered and took comfort from the thought that I could wait for Tim, so long as I had a foothold, and then commit myself to the uncertain strength of my arms and legs for salvation. So I turned my bait-box upside down, and mounting upon that, endeavoured to comfort my spirits, and to be courageous, but submissive to my fate. I thought of death, and what it might bring with it, and I tried to repent of the multiplied iniquities of my almost wasted life; but I found that that was no place for a sinner to settle his accounts. Wretched soul, pray I could not.

'The water had not got above my ankles, when, to my inexpressible joy, I saw a sloop bending down towards me, with the evident intention of picking me up. No man can imagine what were the sensations of gratitude which filled my bosom at that moment.

'When she got within a hundred yards of the reef, I sung out to the man at the helm to luff up, and lie by, and lower the boat; but to my amazement, I could get no reply, nor notice of my request. I entreated them, for the love of heaven, to take me off; and I promised, I know not what rewards, that were entirely beyond my power of bestowal. But the brutal wretch of a captain, muttering something to the effect of "that he hadn't time to stop," and giving me the kind and sensible advice to pull off my coat and swim ashore, put the helm hard down, and away bore the sloop on the other tack.

'"Heartless villain!" I shrieked out, in the torture of my disappointment; "may God reward your inhumanity."

'The crew answered my prayer with a coarse, loud laugh; and the cook asked me through a speaking trumpet, "If I was not afraid of catching cold." – The black rascal!

'It now was time to strip; for my knees felt the cool tide, and the wind dying away, left a heavy swell, that swayed and shook the box upon which I was mounted, so that I had occasionally to stoop, and paddle with my hands against the water in order to preserve my perpendicular. The setting sun sent his almost horizontal streams of fire across the dark waters, making them gloomy and terrific, by the contrast of his amber and purple glories.

'Something glided by me in the water, and then made a sudden halt. I looked upon the black mass, and, as my eye ran along its dark outline, I saw, with horror, that it was a shark; the identical monster out of whose mouth I had just broken my hook. He was fishing now for me, and was evidently only waiting for the tide to rise high enough above the rock, to glut at once his hunger and revenge. As the water continued to mount above my knees, he seemed to grow more hungry and familiar. At last, he made a desperate dash, and approaching within an inch of my legs, turned upon his back, and opened his huge jaws for an attack. With desperate strength, I thrust the end of my rod violently at his mouth; and the brass head, ringing against his teeth, threw him back into the deep current, and I lost sight of him entirely. This, however, was but a momentary repulse; for in the next minute he was close behind my back, and pulling at the skirts of my fustian coat, which hung dipping into the water. I leaned forward hastily, and endeavoured to extricate myself from the dangerous grasp; but the monster's teeth were too firmly set, and his immense strength nearly drew me over. So, down flew my rod, and off went my jacket, devoted peace offerings to my voracious visitor.

'In an instant, the waves all round me were lashed into froth and foam. No sooner was my poor old sporting friend drawn under the surface, than it was fought for by at least a dozen enormous combatants! The battle raged upon every side. High black fins rushed now here, now there, and long, strong tails scattered sleet and froth, and the brine was thrown up in jets, and eddied and curled, and fell, and swelled, like a whirlpool in Hell-gate.

'Of no long duration, however, was this fishy tourney. It seemed soon to be discovered that the prize contended for contained nothing edible but cheese and crackers, and no flesh; and as its mutilated fragments rose to the surface, the waves subsided into their former smooth condition. Not till then did I experience the real terrors of my situation. As I looked around me to see what had become of the robbers, I counted one, two, three, yes, up to twelve, successively, of the largest sharks I ever saw, floating in a circle around me, like divergent rays, all mathematically equidistant from the rock, and from each other; each perfectly motionless, and with his gloating, fiery eye, fixed full and fierce upon me. Basilisks and rattlesnakes! how the fire of their steady eyes entered into my heart! I was the centre of a circle, whose radii were sharks! I was the unsprung, or rather *unchewed* game, at which a pack of hunting sea-dogs were making a dead point!

'There was one old fellow, that kept within the circumference of the circle. He seemed to be a sort of captain, or leader of the band; or, rather, he acted as the coroner for the other twelve of the inquisition, that were summoned to sit on, and eat up my body. He glided around and about, and every now and then would stop, and touch his nose against some one of his comrades, and seem to consult, or to give instructions as to the time and mode of operation. Occasionally, he would skull himself up towards me, and examine the condition of my flesh, and then again glide back, and rejoin the troupe, and flap his tail, and have another confabulation. The old rascal had, no doubt, been out into the highways and byways, and collected this company of his friends and kinfish, and invited them to supper.

'I must confess, that horribly as I felt, I could not help but think of a tea party, of demure old maids, sitting in a solemn circle, with their skinny hands in their laps, licking their expectant lips, while their hostess bustles about in the important functions of her preparations. With what an eye have I seen such appurtenances of humanity survey the location and adjustment of some especial condiment, which is about to be submitted to criticism and consumption.

'My sensations began to be, now, most exquisite indeed; but I will not attempt to describe them. I was neither hot nor cold, frightened nor composed; but I had a combination of all kinds of feelings and emotions. The present, past, future, heaven, earth, my father and mother, a little girl I knew once, and the sharks, were all confusedly mixed up together, and swelled my crazy brain almost to bursting. I cried, and laughed, and spouted, and screamed for Tim Titus.

'In a fit of most wise madness, I opened my broad-bladed fishing knife, and waved it around my head with an air of defiance. As the tide continued to rise, my extravagance of madness mounted. At one time, I became persuaded that my tide-waiters were reasonable beings, who might be talked into mercy and humanity, if a body could only hit upon the right text. So, I bowed, and gesticulated, and threw out my hands, and talked to them, as friends, and brothers, members of my family, cousins, uncles, aunts, people waiting to have their bills paid; I scolded them as my servants; I abused them as duns; I implored them as jurymen sitting on the question of my life; I congratulated, and flattered them as my comrades upon some glorious enterprise; I sung and ranted to them, now as an actor in a play-house, and now as an elder at a camp-meeting; in one moment, roaring,

On this cold flinty rock I will lay down my head,—

and in the next, giving out to my attentive hearers for singing, a hymn of Dr. Watts so admirably appropriate to the occasion:

On slippery rocks I see them stand,
While fiery billows roll below.

[32]

'What said I, what did I not say! Prose and poetry, scripture and drama, romance and ratiocination – out it came. *"Quamdiu, Catalina, nostra patientia abutere?"* – I sung out to the old captain, to begin with: "My brave associates, partners of my toil," – so ran the strain. "On which side soever I turn my eyes," – "Gentlemen of the jury," – "I come not here to steal away your hearts," – "You are not wood, you are not stones, but" – "Hah!" – "Begin, ye tormentors, your tortures are vain," – "Good friends, sweet friends, let me not stir you up to any sudden flood," – "The angry flood that lashed her groaning sides," – "Ladies and gentlemen," – "My very noble and approved good masters," – "Avaunt! and quit my sight; let the earth hide ye," – "Lie lightly on his head, O earth!" – "O, heaven and earth, that it should come to this!" – "The torrent roared, and we did buffet it with lusty sinews, stemming it aside and oaring it with hearts of controversy," – "Give me some drink, Titinius," – "Drink, boys, drink, and drown dull sorrow," – "For liquor it doth roll such comfort to the soul," – "Romans, countrymen and lovers, hear me for my cause, and be silent that you may hear," – "Fellow citizens, assembled as we are upon this interesting occasion, impressed with the truth and beauty," – "Isle of beauty, fare thee well," – "The quality of mercy is not strained," – *"Magna veritas et prevalebit,"* – "Truth is potent, and" – "Most potent, grave, and reverend seigniors,"—

> Oh, now you weep, and I perceive you feel
> The dint of pity; these are gracious drops.
> Kind souls! what! weep you when you but behold
> Our Caesar's vesture wounded,—

Ha! ha! ha! – and I broke out in a fit of most horrible laughter, as I thought of the mincemeat particles of my lacerated jacket.

'In the meantime, the water had got well up towards my shoulders, and while I was shaking and vibrating upon my uncertain foot-hold, I felt the cold nose of the captain of the band snubbing against my side. Desperately, and without a definite object, I struck my knife at one of his eyes, and, by some singular fortune, cut it out clean from the socket. The shark darted back, and halted. In an instant, hope and reason came to my relief; and it occurred to me, that if I could only blind the monster, I might yet escape. Accordingly, I stood ready for the next attack. The loss of an eye did not seem to affect him much, for after shaking his head once or twice, he came up to me again, and when he was about half an inch off, turned upon his back. This was the critical moment. With a most unaccountable presence of mind, I laid hold of his nose with my left hand, and with my right scooped out his remaining organ of vision. He opened his big mouth, and champed his long teeth at me, in despair. But it was all over with him. I raised my right foot and gave him a hard shove, and he glided off into deep water, and went to the bottom.

'Well, gentlemen, I suppose you'd think it a hard story, but it's none the less a fact, that I served every remaining one of those nineteen sharks in the same fashion. They all came up to me, one by one, regularly and in order, and I scooped their eyes out, and gave them a shove, and they went off into deep water, just like so many lambs. By the time I had scooped out and blinded a couple of dozen of them, they began to seem so scarce that I thought I would swim for the island, and fight the rest for fun, on the way; but just then, Tim Titus hove in sight, and it had got to be almost dark, and I concluded to get aboard and rest myself!'

3

THE MONSTROUS TROUT

by Jerome K. Jerome

THE novel, *Three Men in a Boat* written by Jerome K. Jerome just one hundred years ago in 1889, has rightly been described as a modern classic of farce and it can be enjoyed as much today as when it first appeared. It is pure escapist literature mirroring as it does the wish of many people to get away from the pressures of everyday life and laze away the summer days following whatever is their heart's desire.

Jerome K. Jerome, who was actually born in Walsall, had a wonderful appreciation of the English sense of humour, and after having been a clerk, schoolmaster, reporter, actor and journalist, concentrated on humorous writing and in 1892 became joint-editor of *The Idler* magazine which for some years challenged the popularity of *Punch*. Jerome was a man who loved fishing and 'messing about in boats' and from this love came books such as *Three Men in a Boat*, *The Idle Thoughts of an Idle Fellow* (also 1889) and *Three Men on the Bummel* (1900). In fact, incidents featuring angling are to be found in all these books – but there is no episode quite as funny as the one which follows from *Three Men in a Boat* about a huge fish grandly displayed in a pub and variously claimed to have been landed by not one but several different customers! The denoument to 'The Monstrous Trout' is one that still makes me chuckle even after having read the story a good few times!

THE MONSTROUS TROUT

We stayed two days at Streatley, and got our clothes washed. We had tried washing them ourselves, in the river, under George's superintendence, and it had been a failure. Indeed, it had been more than a failure, because we were worse off after we had washed our clothes than we were before. Before we had washed them, they had been very, very dirty, it is true; but they were just wearable. *After* we had washed them – well, the river between Reading and Henley was much cleaner, after we had washed our clothes in it, than it was before. All the dirt contained in the river between Reading and Henley we collected, during that wash, and worked it into our clothes.

The washerwoman at Streatley said she felt she owed it to herself to charge us just three times the usual prices for that wash. She said it had not been like washing, it had been more in the nature of excavating.

We paid the bill without a murmur.

The neighbourhood of Streatley and Goring is a great fishing centre. There is some excellent fishing to be had here. The river abounds in pike, roach, dace, gudgeon, and eels, just here; and you can sit and fish for them all day.

Some people do. They never catch them. I never knew anybody catch anything up the Thames, except minnows and dead cats, but that has nothing to do, of course, with fishing! The local fisherman's guide doesn't say a word about catching anything. All it says is the place is 'a good station for fishing'; and from what I have seen of the district, I am quite prepared to bear out this statement.

There is no spot in the world where you can get more fishing, or where you can fish for a longer period. Some fishermen come here and fish for a day, and others stop and fish for a month. You can hang on and fish for a year, if you want to: it will be all the same.

The *Angler's Guide to the Thames* says that 'jack and perch are also to be had about here,' but there the *Angler's Guide* is wrong. Jack and perch may *be* about there. Indeed, I know for a fact that they are. You can *see* them there in shoals, when you are out for a walk along the banks; they come and stand half out of the water with their mouths open for biscuits. And, if you go for a bathe, they crowd round, and get in your way and irritate you. But they are not to be 'had' by a bit of worm on the end of a hook, nor anything like it – not they!

I am not a good fisherman myself. I devoted a considerable amount of attention to the subject at one time, and was getting on, as I thought, fairly well; but the old hands told me that I should never be any real good at it, and advised me to give it up. They said that I was an extremely neat thrower, and that I seemed to have plenty of gumption for the thing, and quite enough constitutional laziness. But they were sure I should never make anything of a fisherman. I had not got sufficient imagination.

They said that as a poet, or a shilling shocker, or a reporter, or anything of that kind, I might be satisfactory, but that, to gain any position as a Thames angler, would require more play of fancy, more power of invention than I appeared to possess.

Some people are under the impression that all that is required to make a good fisherman is the ability to tell lies easily and without blushing; but this is a mistake. Mere bald fabrication is useless; the veriest tyro can manage that. It is in the circumstantial detail, the embellishing touches of probability, the general air of scrupulous – almost of pedantic – veracity, that the experienced angler is seen.

Anybody can come in and say, 'Oh, I caught fifteen dozen perch yesterday evening'; or 'Last Monday I landed a gudgeon, weighing eighteen pounds, and measuring three feet from the tip to the tail.'

There is no art, no skill, required for that sort of thing. It shows pluck, but that is all.

No; your accomplished angler would scorn to tell a lie, that way. His method is a study in itself.

He comes in quietly with his hat on, appropriates the most comfortable chair, lights his pipe, and commences to puff in silence. He lets the youngsters brag away for a while, and then, during a momentary lull, he removes the pipe from his mouth, and remarks, as he knocks the ashes out against the bars:

'Well, I had a haul on Tuesday evening that it's not much good my telling anybody about.'

'Oh! why's that?' they ask.

'Because I don't expect anybody would believe me if I did,' replies the old fellow calmly, and without even a tinge of bitterness in his tone, as he refills his pipe, and requests the landlord to bring him three of Scotch, cold.

There is a pause after this, nobody feeling sufficiently sure of himself to contradict the old gentleman. So he has to go on by himself without any encouragement.

'No,' he continues thoughtfully; 'I shouldn't believe it myself if anybody told it to me, but it's a fact, for all that. I had been sitting there all the afternoon and had caught literally

[38]

nothing – except a few dozen dace and a score of jack; and I was just about giving it up as a bad job when I suddenly felt a rather smart pull at the line. I thought it was another little one, and I went to jerk it up. Hang me, if I could move the rod! It took me half an hour – half an hour, sir! – to land that fish; and every moment I thought the line was going to snap! I reached him at last, and what do you think it was? A sturgeon! a forty pound sturgeon! taken on a line, sir! Yes, you may well look surprised – I'll have another three of Scotch, landlord, please.'

And then he goes on to tell of the astonishment of everybody who saw it; and what his wife said, when he got home, and of what Joe Buggles thought about it.

I asked the landlord of an inn up the river once, if it did not injure him, sometimes, listening to the tales that the fishermen about there told him; and he said:

'Oh, no; not now, sir. It did used to knock me over a bit at first, but, lor love you! me and the missus we listens to 'em all day now. It's what you're used to, you know. It's what you're used to.'

I knew a young man once, he was a most conscientious fellow and, when he took to fly fishing, he determined never to exaggerate his hauls by more than twenty-five per cent.

'When I have caught forty fish,' said he, 'then I will tell people that I have caught fifty, and so on. But I will not lie any more than that, because it is sinful to lie.'

But the twenty-five per cent. plan did not work well at all. He never was able to use it. The greatest number of fish he ever caught in one day was three, and you can't add twenty-five per cent to three – at least, not in fish.

So he increased his percentage to thirty-three-and-a-third, but that, again, was awkward, when he had only caught one or two; so, to simplify matters, he made up his mind to just double the quantity.

He stuck to this arrangement for a couple of months, and then he grew dissatisfied with it. Nobody believed him when he told them that he only doubled, and he, therefore, gained no credit that way whatever, while his moderation put him at a disadvantage among the other anglers. When he had really caught three small fish, and said he had caught six, it used to make him quite jealous to hear a man, whom he knew for a fact had only caught one, going about telling people he had landed two dozen.

So, eventually he made one final arrangement with himself, which he has religiously held to ever since, and that was to count each fish that he caught as ten, and to assume ten to begin with. For example, if he did not catch any fish at all, then he said he had caught ten fish – you could never catch less than ten fish by his system; that was the foundation of it. Then, if by any chance he really did catch one fish, he called it twenty, while two fish would count thirty, three forty, and so on.

It is a simple and easily worked plan, and there has been some talk lately of its being made use of by the angling fraternity in general. Indeed, the Committee of the Thames Anglers' Association did recommend its adoption about two years ago, but some of the older members opposed it. They said they would consider the idea if the number were doubled, and each fish counted as twenty.

If ever you have an evening to spare, up the river, I should advise you to drop into one of the little village inns, and take a seat in the tap-room. You will be nearly sure to meet one or two old rod-men, sipping their toddy there, and they will tell you enough fishy stories in half an hour to give you indigestion for a month.

George and I – I don't know what had become of Harris; he had gone out and had a shave, early in the afternoon, and had then come back and spent full forty minutes in pipe-claying his shoes, we had not seen him since – George and I, therefore, and the dog, left to ourselves, went for a walk to Wallingford on the second evening, and coming home, we called in at a little riverside inn, for a rest, and other things.

We went into the parlour and sat down. There was an old

fellow there, smoking a long clay pipe, and we naturally began chatting.

He told us that it had been a fine day today and we told him that it had been a fine day yesterday, and then we all told each other that we thought it would be a fine day tomorrow; and George said the crops seemed to be coming up nicely.

After that it came out, somehow or other, that we were strangers in the neighbourhood, and that we were going away the next morning.

Then a pause ensued in the conversation, during which our eyes wandered round the room. They finally rested upon a dusty old glass-case, fixed very high up above the chimney-piece, and containing a trout. It rather fascinated me, that trout; it was such a monstrous fish. In fact, at first glance, I thought it was a cod.

'Ah!' said the old gentleman, following the direction of my gaze, 'fine fellow that, ain't he?'

'Quite uncommon,' I murmured; and George asked the old man how much he thought it weighed.

'Eighteen pounds six ounces,' said our friend, rising and taking down his coat. 'Yes,' he continued, 'it wur sixteen year ago, come the third o' next month, that I landed him. I caught him just below the bridge with a minnow. They told me he wur in the river, and I said I'd have him, and so I did. You don't see many fish that size about here now, I'm thinking. Good night, gentlemen, good night.'

And out he went, and left us alone.

We could not take our eyes off the fish after that. It really was a remarkably fine fish. We were still looking at it, when the local carrier, who had just stopped at the inn, came to the door of the room with a pot of beer in his hand, and he also looked at the fish.

'Good-sized trout, that,' said George, turning round to him.

'Ah! you may well say that, sir,' replied the man; and then, after a pull at his beer, he added, 'Maybe you wasn't here, sir, when that fish was caught?'

[41]

'No,' we told him. We were strangers in the neighbourhood.

'Ah!' said the carrier, 'then, of course, how should you? It was nearly five years ago that I caught that trout.'

'Oh! was it you who caught it, then?' said I.

'Yes, sir,' replied the genial old fellow. 'I caught him just below the lock – leastways, what was the lock then – one Friday afternoon; and the remarkable thing about it is that I caught him with a fly. I'd gone out pike fishing, bless you, never thinking of a trout, and when I saw that whopper on the end of my line, blest if it didn't quite take me aback. Well, you see, he weighed twenty-six pound. Good night, gentlemen, good night.'

Five minutes afterwards a third man came in, and described how *he* had caught it early one morning, with bleak; and then he left, and stolid, solemn-looking, middle-aged individual came in, and sat down over by the window.

None of us spoke for a while; but, at length, George turned to the newcomer, and said:

'I beg your pardon, I hope you will forgive the liberty that we – perfect strangers in the neighbourhood – are taking, but my friend here and myself would be so much obliged if you would tell us how you caught that trout up there.'

'Why, who told you I caught the trout?' was the surprised query.

We said that nobody had told us so, but somehow or other we felt instinctively that it was he who had done it.

'Well, it's a most remarkable thing – most remarkable,' answered the stolid stranger, laughing; 'because, as a matter of fact, you are quite right. I did catch it. But fancy your guessing it like that. Dear me, it's really a most remarkable thing.'

And then he went on, and told us how it had taken him half an hour to land it, and how it had broken his rod. He said he had weighed it carefully when he reached home, and it had turned the scale at thirty-four pounds.

He went in his turn, and when he was gone, the landlord came in to us. We told him the various histories we had heard about his trout, and he was immensely amused, and we all laughed very heartily.

'Fancy Jim Bates and Joe Muggles and Mr. Jones and old Billy Maunders all telling you that they had caught it. Ha! ha! ha! Well, that is good,' said the honest old fellow, laughing heartily. 'Yes, they are the sort to give it *me*, to put up in *my* parlour, if *they* had caught it, they are! Ha! ha! ha!'

And then he told us the real history of the fish. It seemed that he had caught it himself, years ago, when he was quite a lad; not by any art or skill, but by that unaccountable luck that appears to always wait upon a boy when he plays the wag from school, and goes out fishing on a sunny afternoon, with a bit of string tied on to the end of a tree.

He said that bringing home that trout had saved him from a whacking, and that even his schoolmaster had said it was worth the rule-of-three and practice put together.

He was called out of the room at his point, and George and I again turned our gaze upon the fish.

It really was a most astonishing trout. The more we looked at it, the more we marvelled at it.

It excited George so much that he climbed up on the back of a chair to get a better view of it.

And then the chair slipped, and George clutched wildly at the trout-case to save himself, and down it came with a crash, George and the chair on top of it.

'You haven't injured the fish, have you?' I cried in alarm, rushing up.

'I hope not,' said George, rising cautiously and looking about.

But he had. That trout lay shattered into a thousand fragments – I say a thousand, but they may have only been nine hundred. I did not count them.

We thought it strange and unaccountable that a stuffed trout should break up into little pieces like that.

And so it would have been strange and unaccountable, if it had been a stuffed trout, but it was not.

That trout was plaster of Paris.

4
A CATCH ON THE LINE

by R. Andom

Though his work is not as well remembered today as it deserves to be, the books of R. Andom – especially those featuring the comic character, Troddles, and his trio of friends – were tremendously popular with readers from all walks of life around the turn of the century. The name R. Andom – a pseudonym presumably representing 'random' – hid the identity of Alfred Walter Barrett, who like Jerome K. Jerome had graduated through several jobs to become a humorous writer for boys' papers and then weekly periodicals, finally becoming editor of the magazine, *Nuggets*.

Barrett was born in London and appears to have been a keen angler from his childhood for he won a fishing contest on the River Thames when he was only 13! He was also fond of cycling, and some of his earliest stories for *Boys World* magazine featured a group called 'The Waltham Wobblers', each episode subtitled 'The Misadventures of a Boys' Cycling Club'. This group sometimes halted their excursions to do a little fishing – usually with disastrous results!

It was in 1899 that Barrett introduced readers to Troddles who went from one misadventure to another in the company of his friends Murray, Wilks and the anonymous narrator of the tales. The success of these stories caused Barrett – as R. Andom – to be compared with Jerome K. Jerome and another famous fantasist of the period, R. Anstey, and among the successful collections of Troddles stories can be listed,

Troddles and Us – and Others (1899), *Adrift With Troddles* (1901) and *We Three and Troddles* (1905).

Troddles and his companions were involved in a number of fishing episodes, but the story here is my favourite. Perhaps I am a little biased because it happens to be set in Broxbourne, Hertfordshire where I lived for a while and where I first went fishing with my two young sons – so, naturally, it also brings back a few funny *personal* memories . . .

A CATCH ON THE LINE

We wanted to do something, and we thought we would go fishing. We didn't know much about fishing, it is true; but, as Murray somewhat offensively remarked, any fool could sit on the bank and hold a bit of stick over the water.

Wilks said we'd go to Broxbourne. The River Lea is there – a bit of it – he told us, and fishes; and he knew it was a splendid place for catching things. A fellow of his acquaintance once moved out there with his family, and they hadn't been in the place three weeks before they all caught the scarlatina, and the last time he himself was there he caught a magnificent cold. This sounded alluring, and we agreed to go to Brox-bourne and see what *our* luck would be.

Our train, which left Liverpool Street about three, was one of the things that we didn't catch; but there was so much that we did that we could afford to pass that by. To begin with, we caught a most awful wigging from the railway authorities. It sprang in the first instance from an aggrieved porter, who was a victim to Murray's passion for picking up odd fragments of natural laws and illustrating them. While waiting about the platform for the next train, which gave three-quarters of an hour for the proverbial utilisation of idle hands, he illustrated centrifugal force for us with the can of ground-bait we had thoughtfully provided ourselves with. It was cold oatmeal mush, and had been annexed from Mrs Bloggs' pantry in an old beer can by Wilks, who laboured under the delusion that he was quite sufficiently 'up' in all that pertained to the capture of 'tiddlers' to advise and direct us.

Murray slung the can on an old boot-lace and whirled it over and over, at the same time giving us an elaborate and absolutely untruthful reason for the fact that the contents remained passively within it – the can, I mean, not the reason. Of course, all schoolboys are familiar with the experiment, though they may not be enlightened as to cause – being, in fact, very well satisfied with effect – but it was due to centrifu-gal force, Murray explained.

As Wilks afterwards tersely remarked, the reason why the can flew off at an angle and smacked an inoffensive porter in the eye, and smothered him with ground-bait, was due chiefly to the fact that the boot-lace was rotten.

It was irritating and somewhat painful, doubtless, but we thought the porter made quite an unnecessary amount of fuss over it. He could see very well that it was a pure accident, and it isn't dignified to lose your temper and storm at a man who has met with misfortune, even though you suffer from the effects of it. Of course wilful aggression is another matter, and there are occasions when the militant attitude is not only advisable, but necessary.

We had quite a large gathering of officials and passengers round us by the time the porter had done expressing his views, and the sympathy was so obviously with him that we advised Murray to try the soothing effect of a bit of silver, and cleared off and allowed him to take it or not as he deemed best. Anyway, we had lost our ground-bait, and, as Wilks remarked, that was as much as we could be expected to contribute.

Wilks made for the refreshment room, Troddles retreated to get a shave, and I hung about the bookstall, and by the time our train came in Murray had settled the matter to everybody's satisfaction, except his own. He said he recognised that we had some sort of claim on him, and his knowledge was always at the service of humanity; but, all the same, he thought half-a-crown was too much to pay to enlighten our insane intellects on the manifold beauties and wonders of centrifugal force.

I told him that he had not paid for enlightening our intellects, but for darkening the porter's eye, and considering what a lovely splash he had had with that ground-bait I considered that it was a cheap lot.

Murray was inclined to argue the matter, so we shoved him into an empty smoker and sat on him until the train ran out of the station.

A little levity does not come amiss, if it is in season and in bounds; but one might almost as well have charge of a pack of schoolboys as to take Wilks and Murray out for an afternoon. Better in fact, because you could clump their heads and reduce them to order, whereas Murray and Wilks are past the clumpable stage, and haven't sufficient balance to justify an appeal to their sense of dignity.

It was a fairly fast train, and was not timed to stop until we got to Waltham; so Troddles curled himself up in a corner and

[49]

went to sleep, and I monopolised the other and became absorbed in my pipe and a magazine.

When next I came to a recollection of commonplace, ordinary, everyday affairs, we were speeding through Tottenham Station, and Murray was remarking, 'Come out of it, Wilks. If I had known you were going to stick there all the journey, I'd have taken first go.'

I looked up, and found Wilks with a foot on either seat and his head poked out of the lamp-hole in the roof. It struck me as being a particularly silly sort of trick, even then; but Murray assured me that the scenic effect was a striking one, and well worth experiencing, and I made up my mind to have a look, too.

Wilks didn't seem in any hurry to vacate, and Murray, who was getting more and more impatient at his selfishness, pinched his legs to fetch him down. The only effect was to cause Wilks to land out viciously with his foot, and with so much force and precision that it would have spoilt Murray's beauty considerably had the kick taken effect. We shouted up; but, what with his position and the row the train was making, it was evident that Wilks could not hear us.

'Oh, the pig!' grumbled Murray. 'Stick your head out of the window and tell him we want to have a go.'

I did so, and above the din of the train I caught the gist of a wild tirade which brought me in again in double-quick time.

'What does he say?' queried Murray.

'Well, the printable part of it seems to be to the effect that he is wedged up somehow, and that you are a particular sort of ass for doing, or not doing, something or other that you should or shouldn't do,' said I. 'It is a bit disjointed and vague.'

'A big bit,' said Murray drily. 'Here, let's see what's up.'

Murray scrambled on to the seat and gave a mighty tug at Wilks' arm, at the same time yelling a frank and pointed suggestion to him to come in and let us have a go.

Then came down the answer, clear and unmistakable this time, and suggesting a world of latent wrath and some amount of pain.

[50]

'You fat-headed imbecile! don't mess about!' ran some of the tirade. 'Do you think I'm stopping here for the fun of it? I'm wedged up, I tell you, and can't get my head back anyway.'

Murray whistled.

'That's a jolly go,' he murmured rapturously. 'What are we going to do now? If his feet slip he'll be hanged, as sure as fate.'

He prodded Troddles in the ribs and told him to wake up for the execution, and Troddles did wake up. He grumbled a bit until he caught sight of the rigid and idiotic figure standing in the centre of the carriage, with his head through the hole in the top.

'What's Wilks doing there?' he inquired innocently.

'Admiring the scenery,' said Murray. 'He's been admiring it for the last ten minutes, and he'll have to go on doing it for the rest of his life. He's wedged, Troddles, dear. Got caught in, you know, and can't get out. Darned inconvenient thing, too, to have to drag a railway carriage round with you wherever you go for the rest of your days. Uncomfortable to sleep in, I should imagine. I wonder what they'll do? They might cut a piece out of the roof and let him have it for a collar on paying for the damage, I should think. The ring is set in an iron plate, if I know anything about it, and he'll just have to go on wearing it. Fancy, old Wilks might come to live in history, after all – the ass in the iron collar, a companion to the man in the iron mask.'

Murray's pleasantry struck us as being untimely, and we told him to shut up. It seemed to us much more important to give Wilks what assistance we could to help him out of his unpleasant predicament than to waste useful time in gibing at his misfortune; though I had some pretty severe things to say of the childish folly which had caused it. It was funny, I must admit, to see Wilks kick round when Murray tickled his legs, and endeavour to do some of us an injury; but that was also out of place, and I earnestly begged Murray to put the temptation on one side and give serious consideration to the problem of extracting him from the lamp-hole.

Murray was full of resource. When people get a tight ring on their finger, he told us, the usual way is to bind it round firmly with worsted or cotton, and then slip the end under the ring and wind it off. He said he didn't see why we couldn't adopt the same plan; we could wind Wilks up in the fishing-lines; but I didn't consider the plan practical, for obvious reasons. In fact, I thought it an unusually silly suggestion, even for Murray, and I said so, with the result that several useful minutes were lost in pointless recrimination.

Troddles said Wilks ought to move round a bit on his own account, and he pointed out, with some show of reason, that as there had been room for his head to go through there must obviously be room for it to come back again. He got up on the seat and hurled this truism through the roof to Wilks, who growled something inarticulate in reply, and kicked round a bit more just to show us that he was getting impatient and wanted a change of scene and position.

We got up to investigate, too, and by observation and inquiry we elicited the fact that Wilks was held a prisoner by his ears chiefly. He could get back as far as there, and then he wedged, and to try to force the passage was too painful for him to insist on after the first endeavour.

'That's the worst of having such lumping great flappers,' grumbled Murray. 'I always said he had too much ear, and if ever he got into a serious difficulty it would be either through them or his feet.'

Troddles suggested that one of us might climb up on to the roof and hold the projecting members flat while Wilks wriggled down. It was a practical scheme, but Troddles didn't rush to put it into operation, and we didn't feel quite equal to such a risky job as that, even in the sacred cause of friendship.

Murray said if it would rain or something, it would help, because cold made the flesh contract. I said so did a pair of scissors, and I put it to Wilks whether he had not better sacrifice a little superfluous ear and obtain liberty rather than remain fastened to a railway carriage for the rest of his life. As

Murray said, there was such a lot of it that he could very well spare a square foot or so.

Wilks declined the proposal forcibly and none too politely, and just then we ran into Waltham Station. We crowded up round the door to discourage any possible passenger from entering; but a schoolboy, evidently going home after morning term, came to a halt in front of us, and, perhaps liking our appearance, resolved to travel in our company.

He was about fourteen, dressed in an untidy Eton suit, and with an engagingly dirty face, and he stood on the footboard and asked Murray plaintively if we wanted 'all the bally carriage' to ourselves. Murray was so staggered that he gave way and permitted the self-assured youngster to pass us, and he threw his belongings on to the rack and settled down, and produced his cigarette case and asked me to 'have a weed.'

Then the train moved out, and at the same time our small friend caught sight of the lower portion of Wilks and got interested.

'What's he doing?' he queried.

'Mending the roof,' said Murray, mendaciously.

'Rats!' quoth the cheeky youngster. 'He's been sticking his head out, and got it jammed. They all do that, unless they're in the know. We get all the new boys to do it, and then tickle 'em until they buy off. It's no end of a lark; let's try it on him.'

This facetious suggestion was accompanied by a significant upward gesture towards Wilks so that there should be no mistake as to who was meant.

We declined to experiment. It wasn't safe, we told him, and seeing that no fun was likely to be forthcoming, our small friend good-naturedly condescended to entertain us with anecdotes and illustrations of his school life and companions instead, though I could see that we had dropped considerably in his estimation.

This was slow for Wilks, and, after a few minutes, a chance though well-directed kick, which reached Troddles' ribs and made him sing out, apprised us that something was required from above.

'Well, I'm sugared!' said Murray, after listening intently. 'He says he wants a smoke.'

'He'll have to go on wanting,' I observed. 'How does he suppose he's going to get his pipe up there?'

'Hook it on to your fishing rod, ready lit, and drop it over to him from the window, why don't you?' advised our companion.

What that boy didn't know was clearly not worth knowing, and young as he was, he gave magnificent promise of being the sort of companion who would be likely to prove useful in a tight place.

Troddles hooked Wilks' pipe and pouch out of his pocket, and getting it under full steam he handed it to Murray, who fastened it to my rod, and ran a frightful risk of decapitation before he finally came to the conclusion that the plan wasn't feasible. Wilks couldn't do a blessed thing to help himself; and being compelled to cast in the dark, so to speak, it required a skill beyond what we possessed to drop the pipe anywhere near Wilks' mouth though we got it in his eye very successfully, once.

'Oh, well,' said the kid, not to be beaten, 'tell him to shift his long neck, and pass it up the side to him.'

Murray tried again, and after burning Wilks under the chin we contrived to effect the manoeuvre, and Wilks got his smoke.

It must have looked comical, and Troddles was saddened to think that he had left his outfit at home, and so lost the chance of obtaining a snap-shot of it.

The railway people were quite unnecessarily cross about the matter. Of course, it was silly of Wilks, but he knew that well enough without telling him so, and no one could have supposed that he did it just to vex other people. I know that it gave the porters a lot of trouble. They hung on to his legs and bawled at him savagely at first, until Wilks kicked the guard in the jaw and told them that he wasn't going to have his head tugged off just to save them a bit of trouble. They had to break up the train to get the carriage out and run it on to a siding, and then settle down to the business seriously. But it was of no use. Wilks was sore in neck and temper, he wouldn't even try half the likely schemes they propounded, and at last the station-master went off for a carpenter.

'Why not leave him as he is, and show him at a penny a time?' suggested our schoolboy companion, who had alighted with us and stayed by to see the thing out.

We said we wanted him for other purposes, or else we would.

'Oh,' said the boy coolly. 'Well, why don't you get him out, then?'

This was irritating; but Troddles who is generally kind to children, thoughtfully went over the whole thing again and tried to make the kid realise that we didn't because we couldn't.

'Rats!' retorted the animated lump of impudence. 'Tell him to hold his head on one side and draw it down until one ear is disengaged, and then cant over, and he'll come out like greased lightning. You don't need to go cutting up a good railway carriage for a simple thing like that.'

Wisdom from the mouth of babes!

The thing was so obviously simple that I wondered how on earth we could have failed to see it. All the same, I felt a painful desire to get that boy by the ear and pull it just to freshen up his sense of what is due to his elders, and to warn him not to be selfish in future in withholding the tidings of a great device or invention in times of emergency.

Late as it was, having got it, we weren't too uppish to take it. No more was Wilks, and a few minutes more sufficed to put him – raw and bruised from his struggles – inside the carriage again. He seemed to bear us a grudge for the whole thing – as if it had been our fault. As Murray said, if he didn't care about travelling that way, what on earth did he do it for?

Just then the boy, who was looking out of the window, turned round, and remarked casually.

'Here's the station-master coming back with the workman. He's got a slop with him, too, and if I were you I should do a guy out of the door on the off-side, and send my regrets on a post card.'

We gathered up our goods in double sharp time, and scrambled on to the line, boy and all. We just stayed to fasten the door again, and then made tracks in single file across the coal siding over a low fence and out on to the public road.

And that is how we went fishing on that eventful Saturday afternoon, and the only thing caught was a stiff neck and a cold in the left eye – by Wilks.

5

ON DRY COW FISHING

by Rudyard Kipling

RUDYARD KIPLING is acknowledged as one of the greatest English writers of recent times and, among his many outstanding works, the two *Jungle Books* (1894–5) have long been considered classic animal stories. Rudyard was, in fact, fascinated by wild life almost from the day of his birth in India, but it seems likely that he was not introduced to the delights of fishing until the time of his schooling spent in England.

There is more definite information that he started to go fishing regularly after his return to India in 1880 when he began his career as a journalist in Lahore. There are mentions of the sport to be found in some of his early poems and short stories, and who can forget the tale of 'Salmon Bahadur'? Kipling also did a lot of angling during the period he lived in America at the end of the century – especially on the great Columbia River between the states of Oregon and Washington where, he has written, he spent many happy hours fly fishing in 1899. (This fact is referred to in the story which follows.) By the time he returned to live permanently in England at Burwash in Sussex, he was an expert fisherman, and he continued his love affair with rod and line for the rest of his life.

Kipling is not, of course, noted as a humorous writer, but after an extraordinary experience while out fishing one day in England, he wrote the following delightful comic tale. He submitted it to *The Fishing Gazette*, and the Editor was more than happy to publish it in his issue of December 13, 1890.

Apart from a reprint in that same publication in May 1951, 'On Dry Cow Fishing' has never appeared in Kipling's Collected Works nor been previously anthologised. It is, therefore, a special pleasure for me to be able to bring this humorous little gem by a master of literature back into print in the pages which follow. . .

ON DRY COW FISHING

It must be clearly understood that I am not at all proud of this performance. In Florida men sometimes hook and land, on rod and tackle a little finer than a steam-crane and chain, a mackerel-like fish called 'tarpon,' which sometimes run up to 120 lb. Those men stuff their captures and exhibit them in glass cases and become puffed up. On the Columbia River sturgeon of 150 lb. weight are taken with the line. When the sturgeon is hooked the line is fixed to the nearest pine tree or steamboat wharf, and after some hours or days the sturgeon surrenders himself, if the pine or line do not give way. The owner of the line then states on oath that he has caught a sturgeon, and he, too, becomes proud.

These things are mentioned to show how light a creel will fill the soul of a man with vanity. I am not proud. It is nothing to me that I have hooked and played 700 lb. weight of quarry. All my desire is to place the little affair on record before the mists of memory breed the miasma of exaggeration.

The minnow cost eighteenpence. It was a beautiful quill minnow, and the tackle-maker said that it could be thrown as a fly. He guaranteed further in respect to the triangles – it glittered with triangles – that, if necessary, the minnow would hold a horse. A man who speaks too much truth is just as offensive as a man who speaks too little. None the less, owing to the defective condition of the present law of libel, the tackle maker's name must be withheld.

The minnow and I and a rod went down to a brook to attend to a small jack who lived between two clumps of flags in the most cramped swim that he could select. As a proof that my intentions were strictly honourable, I may mention that I was using a light split-cane rod – very dangerous if the line runs through weeds, but very satisfactory in clean water, inasmuch as it keeps a steady strain on the fish and prevents him from taking liberties. I had an old score against the jack. He owed me two live bait already, and I had reason to suspect him of coming upstream and interfering with a little bleak pool under a horsebridge which lay entirely beyond his sphere of legitimate influence. Observe, therefore, that my tackle and my motives pointed clearly to jack, and jack alone; though I knew that there were monstrous big perch in the brook.

The minnow was thrown as a fly several times, and, owing to my peculiar, and hitherto unpublished, methods of fly throwing, nearly six pennyworth of the triangles came off, either in my coat collar, or my thumb, or the back of my hand. Fly fishing is a very gory amusement.

The jack was not interested in the minnow, but towards twilight a boy opened a gate of the field and let in some twenty or thirty cows and half a dozen cart horses, and they were all very much interested. The horses galloped up and down the field and shook the banks, but the cows walked solidly and breathed heavily, as people breathe who appreciate the Fine Arts.

By this time I had given up all hope of catching my jack fairly, but I wanted the live bait and bleak account settled before I went away, even if I tore up the bottom of the brook. Just before I had quite made up my mind to borrow a tin of chloride of lime from the farmhouse – another triangle had fixed itself in my fingers – I made a cast which for pure skill, exact judgement of distance, and perfect coincidence of hand and eye and brain, would have taken every prize at a bait casting tournament. That was the first half of the cast. The second was postponed because the quill minnow would not return to its proper place, which was under the lobe of my left ear. It had done thus before, and I supposed it was in collision with a grass tuft, till I turned round and saw a large red and white bald-faced cow trying to rub what would be withers in a horse with her nose. She looked at me reproachfully, and her look said as plainly as words: 'The season is too far advanced for gadflies. What is this strange disease?'

I replied, 'Madam, I must apologise for an unwarrantable liberty on the part of my minnow, but if you will have the goodness to keep still until I can reel in, we will adjust this little difficulty.'

I reeled in very swiftly and cautiously, but she would not wait. She put her tail in the air and ran away. It was a purely involuntary motion on my part: I struck. Other anglers may contradict me, but I firmly believe that if a man had foul-hooked his best friend through the nose, and that friend ran, the man would strike by instinct. I struck, therefore, and the reel began to sing just as merrily as though I had caught my jack. But had it been a jack, the minnow would have come

[61]

away. I told the tackle maker this much afterwards, and he laughed and made allusions to the guarantee about holding a horse.

Because it was a fat innocent she-cow that had done me no harm the minnow held – held like an anchor fluke in coral moorings – and I was forced to dance up and down an interminable field very largely used by cattle. It was like salmon fishing in a nightmare. I took gigantic strides, and every stride found me up to my knees in marsh. But the cow seemed to stake along the squashy green by the brook, to skim over the miry backwaters, and to float like a mist through the patches of rush that squirted black filth over my face. Sometimes we whirled through a mob of her friends – there were no friends to help me – and they looked scandalised; and sometimes a young and frivolous cart horse would join in the chase for a few miles, and kick solid pieces of mud into my eyes; and through all the mud, the milky smell of kine, the rush and the smother, I was aware of my own voice crying: 'Pussy, pussy, pussy! Pretty pussy! Come along then, puss-cat!' You see it is so hard to speak to a cow properly, and she would not listen – no, she would not listen.

Then she stopped, and the moon got up behind the bollards to tell the cows to lie down; but they were all on their feet, and they came trooping to see. And she said, 'I haven't had my supper, and I want to go to bed, and please don't worry me.' And I said, 'The matter has passed beyond any apology. There are three courses open to you, my dear lady. If you'll have the common sense to walk up to my creel I'll get my knife and you shall have all the minnow. Or, again, if you'll let me move across to your near side, instead of keeping me so coldly on your off side, the thing will come away in one tweak. I can't pull it out over your withers. Better still, go to a post and rub it out, dear. It won't hurt much, but if you think I'm going to lose my rod to please you, you are mistaken.' And she said, 'I don't understand what you are saying. I am very, very unhappy.' And I said: 'It's all your fault for trying to fish. Do go to the nearest gate-post, you nice fat thing, and rub it out.'

For a moment I fancied she was taking my advice. She ran away, and I followed. But all the other cows came with us in a bunch, and I thought of Phaeton trying to drive the Chariot of the Sun, and Texan cowboys killed by stampeding cattle, and 'Green Grow the Rushes, oh!' and Solomon and Job, and 'loosing the bands of Orion,' and hooking Behemoth, and Wordsworth who talks about whirling round with stones and rocks and trees, and 'Here we go round the Mulberry Bush,' and 'Pippin Hill,' and 'Hey Diddle Diddle,' and most especially the top joint of my rod. Again she stopped – but nowhere in the neighbourhood of my knife – and her sisters stood moonfaced round her. It seemed that she might, now, run towards me, and I looked for a tree, because cows are very different from salmon, who only jump against the line, and never molest the fisherman. What followed was worse than any direct attack. She began to buck-jump, to stand on her head and her tail alternately, to leap into the sky, all four feet together, and to dance on her hind legs. It was so violent and improper, so desperately unladylike, that I was inclined to blush, as one would blush at the sight of a prominent statesman sliding down a fire escape, or a duchess chasing her cook with a skillet. That flopsome *abandon* might go on all night in the lonely meadow among the mists, and if it went on all night – this was pure inspiration – I might be able to worry through the fishing line with my teeth.

Those who desire an entirely new sensation should chew with all their teeth, and against time, through a best waterproofed silk line, one end of which belongs to a mad cow dancing fairy rings in the moonlight; at the same time keeping one eye on the cow and the other on the top joint of a split cane rod. She buck-jumped and I bit on the slack just in front of the reel; and I am in a position to state that that line was cored with steel wire throughout the particular section which

[63]

I attacked. This has been formally denied by the tackle maker, who is not to be believed.

The *wheep* of the broken line running through the rings told me that henceforth the cow and I might be strangers. I had already bidden good-bye to some tooth or teeth; but no price is too great for freedom of the soul.

'Madam,' I said, 'the minnow and 20 ft. of very superior line are your alimony without reservation. For the wrong I have unwittingly done to you I express my sincere regret. At the same time, may I hope that Nature, the kindest of nurses, will in due season. . . .'

She or one of her companions must have stepped on her spare end of the line in the dark, for she bellowed wildly and ran away, followed by all the cows. I hoped the minnow was disengaged at last; and before I went away looked at my watch, fearing to find it nearly midnight. My last cast for the jack was made at 6.23 p.m. There lacked still three-and-a-half minutes of the half hour; and I would have sworn that the moon was paling before the dawn!

'Simminly someone were chasing they cows down to bottom o' Ten Acre,' said the farmer that evening. ''Twasn't you sir?'

'Now under what earthly circumstances do you suppose I should chase your cows? I wasn't fishing for them, was I?'

Then all the farmer's family gave themselves up to jam-smeared laughter for the rest of the evening, because that was a rare and precious jest, and it was repeated for months, and the fame of it spread from that farm to another, and yet another at least 3 miles away, and it will be used again for the benefit of visitors when the freshets come in the spring.

But to the greater establishment of my honour and glory I submit in print this bald statement of fact, that I may not, through forgetfulness, be tempted later to tell how I hooked a bull on a Marlow Buzz, how he ran up a tree and took to water, and how I played him along the London road for 30 miles, and gaffed him at Smithfield. Errors of this kind may

[64]

creep in with the lapse of years, and it is my ambition ever to be a worthy member of that fraternity who pride themselves on never deviating by one hair's breadth from the absolute and literal truth.

6

THE LEGACY OF NOAH'S ART

by Harry Graham

REGINALD DRAKE BIFFIN, the central character in this next story, has been described by his creator, Harry Graham, as 'a chap who knows something about everything and everything about something.' His exploits in the pages of magazines and books during the first half of this century earned him a lot of fans – and among the most successful of the stories were those in which Biffin displayed his prowess at one sport or another. In fact, a selection of these sporting chronicles were collected in a volume called *The Complete Sportsman* which appeared in 1914 and has been much sought after ever since.

The author, Harry Graham, was himself a keen sportsman in his younger days, though angling appears to have been one of the few activities he continued into old age. He was also something of an armchair fisherman, too, reading all the famous instructional books on angling as well as making a study of the history of the sport. The knowledge he garnered has been humorously linked with another chapter in the career of Reginald Biffin in Graham's inimitable way in the pages which follow. I think that even the most knowledgeable fisherman who believes he has a sound understanding of the sport's history is in for a few surprises in 'The Legacy of Noah's Art' . . .

THE LEGACY OF NOAH'S ART

I.

Besides being the most ancient and honourable of all human pastimes, fishing is the only form of sport that has been continuously practised without a break since the very creation of the universe.

The climatic conditions that prevailed at the time of the

Flood rendered it almost impossible for the sportsmen of that period to take part in those pursuits to which Adam and his immediate descendants had devoted so much of their leisure in those happy days when the Eden coverts were still carefully preserved. The persistent succession of rainy days made deer-stalking an unpleasant as well as an unprofitable amusement; as the tide gradually rose it became too damp for anything but snipe-shooting and otter-hunting, and, finally, when nearly the whole surface of the world had been submerged, every variety of game was driven to the mountain tops, where they clustered together in pathetic groups which could prove tempting to none but the most flagrant pot-hunter. It is said that when the flood eventually reached the summit of Mount Ararat, that eminence was so thickly infested with big game that it would have been impossible to throw one's hat out of any window of the ark without hitting a wild animal of some kind or another, and a shot fired at random 'into the brown' would have brought down at least a dozen specimens of the world's rarest *fauna*.

The prospect of anything in the form of a massacre was not likely to appeal to so thorough a sportsman as Noah, and when that worthy man had stowed his menagerie safely on board the ark he turned his whole attention to the capture of those denizens of the briny deep upon which his party was fated to rely for sole subsistence until the waters had sensibly subsided. It is, indeed, largely due to the fish diet upon which Noah and his family lived at this period that their descendants have acquired that colossal brain power which finds its expression today within the covers of such a volume as the reader now holds in his hand.

The modern angler, who delicately throws a 'dry fly' over some translucent, willow-fringed trout stream, may sneer at the ponderous piscatorial methods of his less dexterous ancestors. But it must always be remembered that at the time when Noah fished for his daily bread – or, rather, his daily bream – there was not a single dry fly to be had. The only two flies resident in the Ark had got thoroughly wet through long before they came on board, and to supply the existing deficiency of bait by sacrificing one of these valuable lepidoptera, upon whose survival the whole future of their race depended, would in any case have been the height of folly.

That some such solution of the problem crossed the mind of Japhet (the expert fisherman of the party) we have good reason for believing. As he turned a contemplative eye upon the various animals in his charge, seeking to determine which of them would prove the most suitable decoration for the bare fish-hook that he held in his hand, a perceptible shudder ruffled the surface of that sheltered community; the two worms who were lying half asleep in an upper bunk on the saloon deck, huddled more closely together for mutual comfort and support; the breathing of the ants came quick and sharp; and you could almost hear the beating of the caterpillars' hearts. It was, indeed, an auspicious moment for all the inmates of that floating palace, where so many couples lived together in what Ham facetiously described as 'canoebial bliss,' when the female wasp of the establishment unexpectedly became the happy mother of thirty fine boy grubs, several of whom it was rightly deemed permissible to make use of as ground-bait.

From that moment the Ark was always well provided with fresh food; its human inhabitants spent many happy hours fishing over the side, and, like that eminent British angler whose name is now a household word (though for the moment I cannot recollect it), found this edifying pastime 'a rest to the mind, a cheerer of the spirits, a diverter of sadness, a moderator of passions, a producer of contentedness, and a begetter of those habits of peace and perseverance upon which so much of human felicity depends.'

Thus it was that fishing became a universally popular pursuit; Japhet's creel fell upon the shoulders of a long line of worthy successors, from St. Peter to Sir Henry Wotton, from Mr. Isaak Walton to Sir Edward Grey and Mr. Harry Tate, and

thence to my uncle, Sir Noel Biffin, than who (or "whom," if
you prefer to be ungrammatical) no modern angler ever
watched a float or impaled a worm upon a bent pin with
greater patience or precision.

II

The subject of fishing divides itself naturally under four
headings: tackle, bait, modes of procedure, and – I shall
remember the fourth presently. Of these the first, though
undoubtedly the most important, is by no means the easiest
upon which to dogmatise satisfactorily.

It must, of course, be obvious that no two kinds of fish, and
no two methods of angling demand the use of the same tackle;
that it would be as foolish to trawl for tarpon with a light ten-
foot split-cane trout rod and a thin horsehair cast, as it would
be to sniggle for lithe and saith (whatever these may be) with
a wire cable attached to a hop-pole. To dwell upon a
commonplace of this kind would be to waste my valuable time
and weary the reader, and though the latter be a minor consideration, it is one which in certain circumstances should not
be entirely overlooked. It will therefore be sufficient for my
purpose to limit this dissertation upon fishing tackle to a few
words of counsel and warning, based upon a wide experience
of every form and variety of angling gear with which it has
been my good fortune to become acquainted in the course of a
long and (I trust) not altogether futile career.

Whether ordinary horsehair or the gut of the silkworm
provides the best material for those 'casts' or 'traces' (as they
are sometimes called), upon which the angler must to so great
an extent rely for any success that he may achieve with rod

and line, is a mere matter of individual taste. Some experts hold one view, while others (equally worthy, honourable, and scrupulous men) feel bound to maintain a totally opposite opinion. I am personally inclined to support both parties; for although the product of the silkworm may be as hyaline and glabrous as any equine capillament, the latter may possess those sequaceous properties which counterbalance the natural lubricity that characterizes the former, and *vice versa*. But whichever form of material it is decided to make use of, the absolute necessity of exercising the greatest care and caution in its selection cannot be too strongly urged. If horsehair be chosen, it should be obtained from the tails of those massive steeds which are commonly harnessed to brewers' drays, and not on any account from cavalry chargers, pit ponies, or the emaciated crocks that still languish obscurely between the shafts of our obsolete hansom-cabs.

An excellent brand of horsehair is that which is supplied for surgical purposes, to stitch up wounds and so forth. In my youth I often obtained a stock of this material from a well-known chemist named Potasch, who kept a small shop in a by-street not far from Piccadilly Circus. The worthy druggist was himself a keen devotee of angling, and while waiting for my change I would constantly engage him in conversation upon the subject. It did not take me long to discover that he possessed all those moral qualities which are as useful to the fisherman as to the chemist: he was a philosopher, took a cheerful view of life, and had that happy knack of procuring the maximum amount of profit with the minimum of expenditure which is as much the key to success on the river bank as behind the counter of a druggery.

I remember being particularly struck on one occasion by his business methods. A rather seedy-looking individual entered the shop while I was there, and asked to be supplied with something that would cure indigestion. The chemist at once proceeded to concoct a pink mixture from the numerous large bottles that stood in a row on a long shelf behind him. To a little of the contents of a vessel labelled 'Grobelia Inflata' he added a few crystals of 'Hyp. Phos. Sod.,' poured in two or three drops of 'Aq. Pur.' and a dash of 'Tinct. Amm.,' measured out a dozen grains of 'Potass. Chlor.' and 'Tart. Ac.,' emptied the decoction into a small glass bottle, secured the cork with sealing wax and string, made a neat paper parcel of the whole thing, using more string and sealing wax, and handed it with a polite bow to his customer.

'How much?' the latter inquired gruffly.

'Two shillings, if you please,' said the druggist.

'Two shillings!' repeated the other indignantly. 'What on earth do you take me for?'

With these words the man flung a threepenny bit upon the counter, picked up the bottle of medicine, and bolted from the shop.

I was naturally somewhat surprised by such extraordinary behaviour, but the chemist remained perfectly calm and unmoved. Shrugging his shoulders in a nonchalant manner, he turned to me with that charming smile which had won my heart the very first time I ever bought one of his porous plasters.

'After all,' he remarked philosophically, 'I've made twopence over the transaction, so I needn't complain.'

It is, as I have said, qualities such as my friend then displayed that make for success both in angling and drugging, and I was not surprised a year or two ago to learn that Mr Potasch was retiring from business an extremely wealthy man, and had been unanimously elected a Patron of the Home for Inebriate Fishermen which the late Sir Findon Haddough founded on the banks of the Thames. His name appeared in a prominent position among the knights in the last New Year's Honours List, and shortly afterwards, when I happened to attend the annual *conversazione* held at the Brighton Aquarium by the Association of Anglo-Saxon Anglers, I was delighted to notice, in a corner of the room, under the banner bearing the motto of the Association (*Non angeli sed angleri*), my old friends Sir Permanganate and Lady Potasch conversing affably with such eminent persons as Dr Nux and Lady Vomica Squills, and the Bishop of Soda and Mint.

The best way of procuring ordinary horsehair is for the angler, accompanied by a trusty friend, with their hats drawn well over their eyes, to hang about the threshold of some big brewery shortly after dawn. As the first waggon-load of casks issues from the gates, the fisherman should step nimbly forward and make a remark of a grossly offensive character to the leading drayman, dwelling perhaps on the latter's extraordinary resemblance to an organ-grinder's monkey, on his dubious parentage and obviously intemperate habits. Being a naturally passionate man, the driver will probably leap down from his perch without further ado, and offer to knock his traducer's head off. While the poor fellow is thus pleasantly engaged, and his attention has been temporarily diverted from his duties, the angler's accomplice should creep up behind the leading horse, wrench a handful of hair from that reluctant creature's tail, and escape at top speed into the offing, with his booty tightly clasped to his bosom. Later on in the day, when the angler has eventually calmed the indignant drayman by explaining to him that he mistook him for his brother, the two accomplices can meet at some appointed spot, and share the spoils without further interruption.

If, on the other hand, it is decided to use gut as the most efficient fabric for casts, there is no better way of ensuring the provision of perfect material than by keeping a small private herd of silkworms, from which the necessary product can be obtained fresh every day to meet the fisherman's requirements. These docile and industrious little creatures are very tame and easy to manage, will soon learn to eat mulberry leaves out of their master's hand, and can be taught to perform a number of entertaining tricks calculated to while away the longest winter evenings. At his fishing-box in Hampshire, my uncle, Sir Noel Biffin, reared a large flock of silkworms, each of whom he knew by name and grew so fond of that his face would often be suffused with tears when the gamekeeper informed him that the supply of gut was running short, and it became necessary to eviscerate another of his charming pets.

III.

It is the greatest mistake to assume that any sort of line and any kind of gut is good enough to catch a fish with. It is, however, certainly true that in times of stress a broken cast has occasionally been satisfactorily mended with a boot-lace; and I have even heard tell of an angler who had left his tackle box at home spending a not altogether unprofitable morning fishing for eels with a pair of braces to which he had fastened a safety pin baited with a ham sandwich. Indeed, my uncle, Horace Biffin, never tires of repeating the story of the ten-pound grilse which he played for over three hours on the end of a thin line of twisted silk that he obtained in so curious a fashion as to merit description.

One summer's evening, two or three years ago, Uncle Horace made up a cheery little play-party, consisting of his wife, his sister Jane and myself, to visit that popular modern comedy, 'Infrequent Mary,' which was then being played to crowded houses at one of the best known of our West End theatres.

We were unable to get four stalls all together, but managed to secure two in the front row and two others immediately behind them. Uncle Horace was naturally averse from sitting next to his wife, and as the society of his sister seemed equally distasteful to him, the two ladies were persuaded to occupy the front seats, while the male members of the party sat in the two others in rear.

[75]

At the beginning of the second act I happened to notice that a small thread of silk was sticking out of the top of Aunt Sophie's gown at the back. I pointed this out to her husband, and he quickly leant forward and began very gently to pull it out. The thread, however, proved to be very much longer than he expected, and by the time Uncle Horace had extracted several feet of it and there was still no sign of his having reached the end, we realised that he was engaged upon a more arduous and complicated business than had originally been supposed. He would have preferred to avoid any further trouble by putting the thread back, but this was now impossible, and so, with clenched teeth and a determined look on his face, he set himself to reel out yard after yard of silk from the nape of his unconsious spouse's V-shaped bodice. Beyond giving an occasional wriggle, as though someone were tickling her, Aunt Sophie remained unmoved by (and apparently ignorant of) what was happening; she was indeed far too deeply engrossed in the play to appreciate the fact that her husband was producing miles of material from her neck in a fashion which riveted the attention of the other occupants of the theatre and would have made the most expert conjuror green with envy.

For close upon three-quarters of an hour Uncle Horace continued his self-imposed task, growing more and more exhausted as he hauled up furlong after furlong of the thread; while I encouraged and stimulated him by humming a sailor's chanty in his ear whenever he seemed to be flagging. At last the silk came to a sudden end. My companion sank back into his stall with a sigh of relief and his arms full of thread, and when we afterwards wound the latter into a ball it was found to measure no less than 4,637¼ yards in length.

During the interval between the last two acts of the play, Aunt Sophie repeatedly complained of the sudden coldness of the theatre, but gave no other sign that she was aware of anything remarkable having occurred. Uncle Horace, however, confided to me next day that when his wife reached home that night and began to undress she suddenly turned deadly pale, and rang for her maid.

It is impossible for me to repeat the conversation that ensued between these two estimable females on the subject of those intimate undergarments which my Aunt distinctly remembered having donned earlier in the evening, but which had now entirely and miraculously disappeared. Suffice it to say that to this day my poor relative imagines that when she dressed for dinner that night she must have been suffering from an attack of momentary mental aphasia, or she could certainly never have gone to the play in nothing but an evening gown, a petticoat, and a pair of stockings. Uncle Horace, of course, could easily have enlightened her, but there are some things that even the boldest husband shrinks from telling his wife, and one of these is that he intends to go fishing with a line of twisted silk composed exclusively of her *dessous*.

IV

It is generally advisable, if not absolutely necessary, for every angler to possess some slight knowledge of the theory and use of knots before he goes confidently forth to the chase. It will perpetually happen to him that he is called upon to join two lengths of gut together, to repair a broken line, attach hooks to casts, and so on; and clumsy fingers often entail the escape of a big fish and the loss of an expensive fly or a valuable bait.

Without becoming involved in an extensive dissertation on the properties of knots and the science of knotting, I may perhaps assume the truth of the self-evident proposition that, *if any plane closed curve have double points only, in pas-*

sing continuously along the curve from one of these to the same again, an even number of double points has been passed through, and therefore knots which can be deformed into their own perversion may justly and without exaggeration be termed amphicheiral or even paradromic – or indeed anything you like. This fact being once established, we may pass on to the consideration of a knot invented by my Uncle Noel, which fulfils all these conditions, has been found invaluable on a score of occasions, and can therefore be strongly recommended to the reader's notice. Once it has been tied – and I admit that this is a somewhat intricate business – there is no danger of its ever coming undone. Indeed, when an elderly clergyman whom I met once in Hertfordshire asked me to lace his footwear for him one Sunday morning as he did not wish to soil his fingers, my acquaintance with this particular knot enabled me to fasten his boots so securely that he was compelled to sleep in them for nearly a week, and his curate had finally to cut them off his feet in order to stave off imminent mortification.

I can best explain the 'Improved Biffin Knot,' as it is technically termed, by a simple diagram:

METHOD OF TYING.

AFTER TYING.

The method of tying this knot is as follows: *Form an overhand granny knot, pass the end round the standing part and through the bight, take two turns round the park and make a half-hitch through the standing part, lay each end over its own standing part and through the bight, under the standing part beyond the bight, and down through the bight over its own standing part and through the bight. Form a clove hitch with the loose ends, pass them through the bight and through each other, lay one of the ends over the knot beyond the standing part and over the bight, haul the ends taut, and the thing is done.*

Before quitting the subject of fishing tackle it may be as well to offer a word or two of advice upon the use of those waterproof boots, or 'waders', which form so necessary a part of every fly fisher's equipment.

The juvenile practice of donning one's father's best evening shoes, covering these with two pairs of stout stockings, and stepping boldy out into midstream with no further protection against the cold, is calculated to induce bronchial catarrh, scurvy, housemaid's knee, and kindred ailments which leave an indelible mark upon the most robust constitution.

In the heyday of my giddy youth I would often spend sixty or seventy hours a week standing up to my waist in water, flogging the surface of some icy torrent, without giving a thought to the possible evil effects of such foolhardy conduct. Experience has, however, shown me the folly of such proceedings, and today I never venture into the shallowest brook until I have carefully rubbed my feet with cod-liver oil, and encased my legs in thick waterproof waders reaching up to my neck.

Even so it is not always possible to avoid accidents. Once, for instance, when I was paternostering for pike in Perthshire, I inadvertently stepped into a deep hole in the river bed. The water immediately rushed in over the top of my waders, carrying with it a shoal of small minnows (or sticklebacks) that chanced to be in the vicinity. These creatures in their frantic efforts to escape, coursed madly round and round inside my boots, and so tickled and excoriated my legs that I became almost demented, and was afterwards laid up in bed for nearly three weeks with acute inflammation of the hips.

In order to guard against the recurrence of so unpleasant an experience I fastened a stout leather strap round the top of my waders before venturing upon another fishing expedition. The result of this nearly proved fatal. When trying to land a six-pound grayling, on the bonny, bonny banks of Loch Lomond, last spring, I overbalanced myself, lost my footing on a slippery rock, and fell headlong into the water. It is true that the strap round my chest prevented an inrush of fish, but it also checked any escape of air from my waders. The latter consequently became so inflated that they acted as lifebuoys and caused the lower part of my body to float on the top of the loch while my head remained immersed beneath its surface. I should have died miserably of suffocation but for the timely intervention of a passing shepherd, who mistook me for a German dirigible balloon that had been recently observed in the neighbourhood, gaffed me through the waders with his crook, and thus released the pent-up air and enabled me to resume that erect position which distinguishes so many human beings from some of the beasts that perish.

V

We now come to the question of bait, under which category I may include live-bait, dead-bait, white-bait, and the ordinary artificial fly with which every fisherman is familiar.

The choice of suitable bait requires the exercise of common sense as well as some slight knowledge of the habits of different fish. Although it is on record that a perch has been caught with its own eye baited on a hook, it would be crass stupidity for an angler to attempt a repetition of this feat. One might as well imagine that because a captured pike has been known to contain a grandfather's clock, a pianola, seventeen yards of blue ribbon, and a small corkscrew, it is therefore advisable to bait one's hook with a set of false teeth or a harpsichord. It should, however, be borne in mind that certain fish will only look at certain baits. Tarpon, for instance, are very particular as to the food they eat, and can be caught with nothing but the head of a red mullet. Parrot-fish, on the other hand, prefer hemp-seed to any other form of diet, while dogfish express a preference for mutton bones, and it would be futile to attempt to catch the smallest catfish (or kitten-fish, to be academically correct) with anything but bread and milk.

The most common type of live-bait is undoubtedly the ordinary earth- or lob-worm. This is justly considered a succulent morsel by almost every species of fish, and is at once hardy and easily procurable. On warm summer nights lob-worms will be found in large quantities on any lawn or at the edge of garden paths, lying half out of their holes fanning themselves with a blade of grass, or bending gracefully over to slake their thirst with deep draughts of dew from the close-cropped turf at their feet. It then becomes a simple enough matter to creep up behind them in india-rubber tennis shoes, seize them smartly round the waist with the finger and thumb of the right hand, and transfer them to a jam pot or other suitable receptacle.

I have never denied that the threading of a worm upon a steel hook entails a certain amount of suffering, and to the sensitive mind such a process is inevitably fraught with unpleasantness. Mr. H. Cholmondeley-Pennell, perhaps the greatest human authority on bait, has done excellent work in the *Badminton Library* by deploring that unnecessary multi-plication of hooks – a feature of the well-known 'Stewart' tackle – which, as he justly remarks, is apt to 'disfigure the worm and detract from its natural appearance.' No truer word was ever spoken. It requires but a slight effort of the imagin-ation to understand that the too lavish use of hooks is the cause of many a domestic tragedy in the worm world. One can easily picture the return to her fireside of some punctured mother worm, so disfigured by the treatment she has received at human hands that her husband turns away from her in disgust, to transfer his affections elsewhere, while her children fly shrieking from the lawn.

When required for immediate use, worms should be kept in a tin box lined with moss, in which a little brick dust has been carefully sprinkled. This undoubtedly helps them to retain that ruddy, sunburnt complexion which will commend them to the consideration of the most fastidious fish. They should never be carried in the angler's mouth, nor in his trousers pocket with his loose change. Nothing is more tiresome than to be unable to articulate coherently when you desire to give an order to the gillie, and the latter may have justifiable cause for disappointment if, at the end of a long day's sport, a worm is pressed into his open palm in place of the gold coin with which it was the fisherman's intention to reward his services.

In most reputable angling clubs the use of ant's eggs as bait is strictly forbidden, partly because this particular lure is so deadly as to render the capture of fish a ridiculously easy affair, and partly because the robbing of ant-roosts has always been rightly regarded as a distinctly unchivalrous proceeding.

The legality of baiting a line with goldfish has not yet been seriously questioned, but I understand that there exists a strong feeling amongst conjurors that this form of bait should be illegitimatised. Professors of magic depend so entirely for their living upon a continuance of the world's supply of goldfish that they not unjustly claim that any action tending to the extermination of these animals is eminently prejudicial to their interests. There is, however, some talk of the matter being thrashed out in the law courts, where an appeal has already been lodged for what is legally known as the restitution of conjuror's rights, and while the question is *sub judice* it is obviously impossible to discuss it.

It should always be the fisherman's chief aim and object to

keep his live-bait as fresh and lively as possible. For this purpose many authorities recommend the administration of small doses of alcohol. This, however, should not be given with too generous a hand, or the inebriated bait tends to become lachrymose and depressed, and the angler's ends are defeated. It is generally advisable to provide oneself with an additional ration of alcohol in case of emergency, since it demands a superhuman display of self-sacrifice to split one's last whisky-and-soda with a goldfish or apply one's favourite brandy flask to the lips of a swooning minnow. I am, personally, very punctilious in this matter, and never stir from the door until I am assured that a quart bottle of brandy is lying at the bottom of my creel. I must, nevertheless, confess that hitherto the worms in my bait-can have seen little more than the outside of the flagon.

VI

Within the limits of a single chapter it is impossible to deal at any length with the different methods of angling in vogue among fishermen in various portions of the world. But whether it be a man's intention to sniggle for carp, to boggle for bream, to trawl for conger, to blither for cod, to snood for smelts, or merely to plummet for plaice, there are certain rules which he should invariably observe if he wishes to fill his basket.

The bass (and its relative the double-bass) can be hooked with almost any tackle on any kind of a rod, but the deep-sea bass (or *basso profundo*) must always be played *con brio* below the line. In snaring skate, gunnel, octopi, or indeed any kind of ocean fish, from the homely haddock to the much maligned shed (whose position as the parent of the whitebait should surely entitle it to respect) a rod is far more effectual than a hand-line. With the latter it may sometimes happen, when a huge marine monster seizes the bait and bolts for the bed of the ocean at breakneck speed, that the line rushes out so rapidly through the fisherman's grasp as to cause the severest cuticular abrasion. The friction created is sometimes so great as to set the angler's hands on fire or even to amputate a finger.

A friend of mine was once dibbling for gunnets off the Isle of Wight, when an immense conger eel made off with his tackle, and before he could let go of the line his fingers had been completely severed at the knuckles, and fell with a series of dismal splashes into the sea. Portions of the missing limbs were subsequently recovered from the stomachs of various fish caught in the vicinity by the local fishermen, and it was a long time before the inhabitants of the island, as they sat round their humble boards of an evening, ceased to push away their plates of kedgeree untasted, remarking with some bitterness that my poor friend seemed to have a finger in every pie.

I need not point out the obvious dangers incurred by the deep-sea angler who fastens his hand-line to a waistcoat button and then goes to sleep at the bottom of the boat, relying upon being awakened by the struggle of some fish that has swallowed his bait. Should such a man accidentally hook a shark he stands a good chance of being pulled overboard, or, at any rate, of sharing a fate similar to that which befell the late Lord Bloxham, whose lamentable demise recently created so profound an impression upon London society.

'Beau' Bloxham will be remembered as one of the last survivals of those spacious days when members of the peerage were still regarded with respect by an admiring populace. He was always exquisitely groomed (as the lady novelists say) and dressed in a picturesque, if somewhat old-world, fashion. To see him strolling down to the House of Lords at four o'clock of an afternoon, to record his vote against the last legislative measure that had been passed by the House of Commons, exuding seals at every fob, with his shiny hat cocked saucily over one ear, was in itself a liberal sartorial education. It was Lord Bloxham's invariable habit to carry his latchkey in his right-hand trouser-pocket, on a long gold chain, the end of which was securely fastened to one of the buttons to which his braces were attached, and to this custom he owed his untimely decease.

One afternoon last summer, at about half past four, when his parliamentary duties had been punctiliously performed, Lord Bloxham returned home and proceeded in his usual leisurely fashion to insert his latchkey into the front door of Bloxham House, Grosvenor Square. By some unfortunate coincidence, for which Providence can alone be held responsible, Mrs Grindelbaum, who had been paying an afternoon call upon Lady Bloxham, happened at this moment to descend her ladyship's front staircase on her way out. The family butler, with that ceremonious air of a *grand seigneur* which he reserved for the titled and wealthy, flung the front door open for Mrs Grindelbaum to emerge, and the unwitting Lord Bloxham, chained to his latchkey, was precipitated into the front hall at an incredible rate of speed. Fortunately, the gold chain snapped, and like an arrow from the bow the aged peer flew from one end of the front hall to the other, cannoned off Mrs Grindelbaum on to the first footman, rebounded from the first footman on to the third footman, ricocheted off the third footman on to a priceless grandfather's clock, and, after finishing the last ten yards of the course on his back, was brought up short by a portrait of the first Earl of Bloxham (painted by Vandyke) which hung at the end of the passage.

Lord Bloxham was then in his eighty-first year and, being a man of economical habits, had made it his practice, ever since the imposition of the super-tax, to save wear and tear to his false teeth by carrying them in his coat-tail pocket between meals. In the course of their owner's flight across the front hall these articles came into violent contact with numerous pieces of furniture, and by the time Lord Bloxham reached the Vandyke he had been severely bitten no less than six times in various parts of his person. Medical aid was soon forthcoming, but in spite of the efforts of three well-known specialists in hydrophobia, and a visit to the Pasteur Institute in Paris, the patient's injuries proved fatal and he passed away, on his eighty-first birthday, universally mourned and regretted.

VII

In all forms of freshwater fishing concealment is the first requisite of sport. Salmon and trout are especially shy, and if they catch sight of an individual slinking along the river bank with a rod over his shoulder, the wiliest attempts to capture them will prove abortive. It is a very good plan in such circumstances to disguise oneself in the skin of a defunct cow (or horse), and trot along the margin of the stream, waving one's tail in the air and mooing (or neighing, as the case may be). But the difficulty of handling a trout rod effectively while running on all fours may easily be imagined, and on the whole perhaps the practice of getting oneself up to look like a willow, and weeping on the river bank, is to be preferred to the most lifelike bovine imitation.

It is not my intention to dwell upon those modern methods of scientific fishing which are so unsportsmanlike as to provoke the condemnation of all right-minded men. But I should be lacking in my duty to the reader if I forbore to mention the patent recently taken out by a French inventor for angling by means of a telephone – a system which would not be tolerated in any sporting country, and only requires to be described to earn universal reprobation.

Certain fish, it is well known, emit faint sounds when alarmed or distressed: tench continue to croak long after capture, and the herring when engaged in mutual intercourse with his fellows makes a noise like a bereaved mouse. Upon this well-known fact the Frenchman bases his invention, and has contrived an apparatus consisting of a telephone receiver and a detonator, both of which are sunk in the water and connected to a post of observation on the river bank. When any fish pass the receiver a sound of squeaking is distinctly heard above the buzzing of the local bees and the soughing of the trees. The angler thereupon presses a button, the detonator explodes, and the air is filled with fragments of dismembered fish, which can be collected at leisure in a landing net.

I only mention this form of angling to deplore it, being well aware that a slaughter such as I have described would evoke expressions of disgust from the least scrupulous of my readers.*

VIII

The true angler is usually a naturalist as well. He knows the name of every fly that he uses, and every fish that he catches, and will rightly hesitate to express his opinion of the latter's

* The apparatus described above can be obtained for fifty-six francs (carriage paid) from M. Henri Blume, Rue de la Framboise, Aix-la-Chapelle, and I shall be obliged if readers will mention my name when ordering it. I speak from experience when I say that it will be found a most effective substitute for the mayfly, and provide the least competent sportsman with an original and inexpensive means of adding to his bag.

value in mere terms of the kitchen. Unlike the ignorant tiro, he will never throw away with every symptom of disgust a fine cuttlefish that has become entangled in his line. Being well acquainted with the various cephalopodous creatures from which the best marking-ink is manufactured, he takes them all carefully home and gets his wife to mark a dozen of his new evening shirts with them. Nothing escapes his vigilant eye: he studies the domestic life of every finny creature that moves beneath the face of the waters. He can discourse at length and with passionate eloquence upon the maternal habits of the cod, an animal that has no less than 3,687,760 children every year, and in this respect provides many of us with an example which, as Mr. Roosevelt has already declared, we should do well to follow if the human race is not to become extinct at no very distant date. His joys are simple joys, his pleasures simple pleasures. The confirmed angler leads an idyllic existence, surrounded by beautiful scenery, inhaling copious draughts of fresh air, and acquiring physical health at a very small financial outlay. He may employ his thoughts for hours at a time in the noblest studies, enjoy a close communion with nature, and cultivate those higher qualities of the mind that distinguish the fisherman from his less fortunate fellows. If he is unsuccessful from a sporting point of view he can always find comfort in the reflection that he has none to quarrel with but himself. If, on the other hand, he happens one day to stagger home with his basket bursting with fish, he will gain the universal esteem of his fellows, and as a respected member of some local *Angliars' Club* can devote the evening of his life to a meticulous narration of those tales of prowess with rod and line which even the most constant repetition can scarcely rob of their original audacity and imaginative splendour.

7

THE POACHER

by Neil Munro

NEIL MUNRO, the Scottish journalist, novelist and newspaper editor, was born at Inveraray on Loch Fyne and it was in the dazzling blue waters of the lake that he first cast a rod and line from a small boat with his grandfather, reputedly one of the best fishermen in the district. Munro left Inveraray while still a young man to pursue a career in journalism, but always returned to the area each summer for a holiday and was a familiar sight to local anglers. His knowledge of the area was put to good use in the essays and stories he later wrote, many of which were published under the pen-name, Hugh Foulis.

Apart from holding the editor's chair on the *Glasgow Evening News*, Neil Munro also wrote several well received novels including *The Lost Pibroch* (1896) and *John Splendid* (1898), but it is undoubtedly for the creation of the wisecracking old captain, Para Handy, who appeared in short stories in the *Glasgow Evening News* for over twenty years that he is best remembered, and I can do no better than quote from an appreciative article published in that newspaper a few years ago: 'Para Handy survives, for his racy humour is more enduring than the flimsy "wisecrack" comedy of the cinema, more penetrating than the colourless "humour" mechanically evolved by trick writing. He has been discovered absorbing the interest of Cambridge University Dons who set themselves examination papers on his voyages and vernacular. He is cherished by numerous Scottish exiles around the world. And one traveller has confessed to carrying leather-bound copies of the first two Para Handy volumes on all his tours abroad – one in his bag, the other in his pocket!'

Para Handy sails the waters of Scotland in his battered old craft, the *Vital Spark*, carrying many different kinds of cargoes – some of them just the right side of being lawful! He also has a great passion for salmon, and is not above poaching those marvellous fish when the occasion arises. In the story which follows he sets out on just such a mission, but is called upon to display all the cunning and ingenuity for which he is famous to outwit the long arm of the law which follows him . . .

THE POACHER

The *Vital Spark* was lying at Greenock with a cargo of scrap iron, on the top of which was stowed loosely an extraordinary variety of domestic furniture, from bird cages to cottage pianos. Para Handy had just had the hatches off when I came to the quayside, and he was contemplating the contents of his hold with no very pleasant aspect.

'Rather a mixed cargo!' I ventured to say.

'Muxed's no' the word for't,' he said bitterly. 'It puts me in mind of an explosion. It's a flittin' from Dunoon. There would be no flittin's in the *Fital Spark* if she wass my boat. But I'm only the captain, och aye! I'm only the captain, thirty-five shullin's a week and liberty to put on a pea-jecket. To be puttin' scrap iron and flittin's in a fine smert boat like this iss carryin' coals aboot in a coach and twice. It would make any man use Abyssinian language.'

'Abyssinian language?' I repeated, wondering.

'Chust that, Abyssinian language – swearing and the like of that, you ken fine, yoursel', withoot me tellin' you. Fancy puttin' a flittin' in the *Fital Spark*! You would think she wass a coal-laary, and her with two new coats of pent out of my own pocket since the New Year.'

'Have you been fishing?' I asked, desirous to change the subject, which was, plainly, a sore one with the Captain. And I indicated a small fishing net which was lying in the bows.

'Chust the least wee bit touch,' he said, with a very profound wink. 'I have a bit of a net there no' the size of a pocket-naipkin, that I use noo and then at the river-mooths. I chust put it doon – me and Dougie – and whiles a salmon or a sea-troot meets wi' an accident and gets into't. Chust a small bit of a net, no' worth speakin' aboot, no' mich bigger nor a pocket-naipkin. They'll be calling it a splash-net, you ken yoursel' withoot me tellin' you.' And he winked knowingly again.

'Ah, Captain!' I said, 'that's bad! Poaching with a splash-net! I didn't think you would have done it.'

'It's no' me; it's Dougie,' he retorted promptly. 'A fair duvvee for high jeenks, you canna keep him from it. I told him many a time that it wasna right, becaause we might be found oot and get the jyle for't, but he says they do it on aal the smertest yats. Yes, that iss what he said to me – "They do it on aal the first-cless yats; you'll be bragging the *Fital Spark* iss chust ass good ass any yat, and what for would you grudge a splash-net?"'

[92]

'Still it's theft, Captain,' I insisted. 'And it's very, very bad for the rivers.'

'Chust that!' he said complacently. 'You'll likely be wan of them fellows that goes to the hotels for the fushing in the rivers. There's more sport aboot a splash-net; if Dougie wass here he would tell you.'

'I don't see where the sport comes in,' I remarked, and he laughed contemptuously.

'Sport!' he exclaimed. 'The best going. There wass wan time yonder we were up Loch Fyne on a Fast Day, and no' a shop open in the place to buy onything for the next mornin's breakfast. Dougie says to me, "what do you think yoursel' aboot takin' the punt and the small bit of net no' worth mentionin', and going doon to the river mooth when it's dark and seeing if we'll no' get a fush?"

'"It's a peety to be poaching on the Fast Day," I said to him.

'"But it's no' the Fast Day in oor parish," he said. "We'll chust give it a trial, and if there's no fush at the start we'll come away back again." Oh! a consuderate fellow, Dougie; he saw my poseetion at wance, and that I wasna awfu' keen to be fushin' wi' a splash-net on the Fast Day. The end and the short of it wass that when it wass dark we took the net and the punt and rowed doon to the river and began to splash. We had got a fine haul at wance of six great big salmon, and every salmon Dougie would be takin' oot of the net he would be feeling it all over in a droll way, till I said to him, "What are you feel-feelin' for, Dougie, the same ass if they had pockets on them? I'm sure they're all right."

'"Oh, yes," he says, "right enough, but I wass frightened they might be the laird's salmon, and I wass lookin' for the luggage label on them. There's none. It's all right; they're chust wild salmon that nobody planted."

'Weel, we had got chust ass many salmon ass we had any need for whem somebody birled a whustle, and the river watchers put off in a small boat from a point outside of us to catch us. There wass no gettin' oot of the river mooth, so we left the boat and the net and the fush and ran ashore, and by-and-by we got up to the quay and on board the *Fital Spark*, and paaused and consudered things.

'"They'll ken it's oor boat," said Dougie, and his clothes wass up to the eyes in salmon scales.

'"There's no doo't aboot that," I says. "If it wassna the Fast Day I wouldna be so vexed; it'll be an awful disgrace to be found oot workin' a splash-net on the Fast Day. And it's peety aboot the boat, it wass a good boat, I wish we could get her back."

'"Ay, it's a peety we lost her," said Dougie; "I wonder in the wide world who could have stole her when we were doon the fo'c'sle at oor supper?" Oh, a smart fellow, Dougie! when he said that I saw at wance what he meant.

'"I'll go up this meenute and report it to the polis office," I said quite firm, and Dougie said he would go with me too, but that we would need to change oor clothes, for they were covered with fush-scales. We changed oor clothes and went up to the sercheant of polis, and reported that somebody had stolen oor boat. He wass sittin' readin' his Bible, it bein' the Fast Day, wi' specs on, and he kneeked up at us, and said, "You are very spruce, boys, with your good clothes on at this time of the night."

'"We aalways put on oor good clothes on the *Fital Spark* on a Fast Day," I says to him; "it's as little as we can do, though we don't belong to the parish."

'Next day there wass a great commotion in the place aboot some blackguards doon at the river mooth poachin' with a splash-net. The Factor wass busy, and the heid gamekeeper wass busy, and the polis wass busy. We could see them from the dake of the *Fital Spark* goin' aboot buzzin' like bum-bees.

'"Stop you!" said Dougie to me aal of a sudden. "They'll be doon here in a chiffy, and findin' us with them scales on oor clothes – we'll have to put on the Sunday wans again."

'"But they'll smell something if they see us in oor Sunday clothes," I said. "It's no' the Fast Day the day."

'"Maybe no' here," said Dougie, "but what's to hinder it bein' the Fast Day in oor own parish?"

'We put on oor Sunday clothes again, and looked the Almanac to see if there wass any word in it of a Fast Day any place that day, but there wass nothing in the Almanac but tides, and the Battle of Waterloo, and the weather for next winter. That's the worst of Almanacs; there's nothing in them you want. We were fair bate for a Fast Day any place, when The Tar came up and asked me if he could get to the funeral of a cousin of his in the place at two o'clock.

'"A funeral!" said Dougie. "The very thing. The Captain and me'll go to the funeral too. That's the way we have on oor Sunday clothes." Oh, a smert, smert fellow, Dougie!

'We had chust made up oor mind it wass the funeral we were dressed for, and no' a Fast Day any place, when the polisman and the heid gamekeeper came doon very suspeecious, and said they had oor boat. "And what's more," said the gamekeeper, "there's a splash-net and five stone of salmon in it. It hass been used, your boat, for poaching."

'"Iss that a fact?" I says. "I hope you'll find the blackguards," and the gamekeeper gave a grunt, and said somebody would suffer for it, and went away busier than ever. But the polis sercheant stopped behind. "You're still in your Sunday clothes, boys," said he; "what iss the occasion today?"

'"We're going to the funeral," I said.

'"Chust that! I did not know you were untimate with the diseased," said the sercheant.

'"Neither we were," I said, "but we are going oot of respect for Colin." And we went to the funeral, and nobody suspected nothin', but we never got back the boat, for the gamekeeper wass chust needin' wan for a brother o' his own. Och ay! there's wonderful sport in a splash-net.'

8

THE EVERLASTING ANGLER

by Stephen Leacock

STEPHEN LEACOCK requires little introduction to lovers of humour, for few anthologies of comic writing worth the name do not include at least one contribution from his pen. Born in Hampshire, he started his career as a teacher of economics at McGill University, Toronto, where he later became a lecturer. But his wicked sense of humour and love of parody caused him to take occasional breaks from the serious world of economics to write humorous essays and stories for newspapers and magazines which in time made him a household name in North America. When these contributions were later collected in books such as *Nonsense Novels* (1911), *Moonbeams from the Larger Lunacy* (1915) and *Winnowed Wisdom* (1926), he found an even larger audience in the rest of the world.

Leacock always had a slightly disparaging attitude to sport, though he did fish occasionally and loved listening to other anglers delivering anecdotes about their achievements with rod and line. There are several stories and a number of essays which feature fishing among the considerable body of his work, but one of my favourites – and an item perhaps best suited to the requirements of this collection – is 'The Everlasting Angler' which he wrote in 1926. Once again, it neatly underlines the fact that humour is never far away where fishing is concerned . . .

THE EVERLASTING ANGLER

The fishing season will soon be with us. For lovers of fishing this remark is true all the year round. It has seemed to me that it might be of use to set down a few of the more familiar fish stories that are needed by anyone wanting to qualify as an angler. There is no copyright on these stories, since Methuselah first told them, and anybody who wishes may learn them at least and make free use of them.

I will begin with the simplest and best known. Everybody who goes fishing has heard it, and told it a thousand times. It is called:

I

THE STORY OF THE FISH THAT WAS LOST

The circumstances under which the story is best told are these. The fisherman returns after his day's outing with his two friends whom he has taken out for the day, to his summer cottage. They carry with them their rods, their landing net and the paraphernalia of their profession. The fisherman carries also on a string a dirty looking collection of little fish, called by courtesy the 'catch.' None of these little fish really measures more than about seven-and-a-half inches long and four inches round the chest. The fisherman's wife and his wife's sister and the young lady who is staying with them come running to meet the fishing party, giving cries of admiration as they get sight of the catch. In reality they would refuse to buy those fish from a butcher at a cent-and-a-half a pound. But they fall into ecstasies and they cry, 'Oh, aren't they beauties? Look at this big one!' The 'big one' is about eight inches long. It looked good when they caught it, but it has been shrinking ever since, and it looks now as if it had died of consumption. Then it is that the fisherman says, in a voice in which regret is mingled with animation:

'Yes, but say, you ought to have seen the one that we lost. We had hardly let down our lines—'

But it may be interjected here that all fishermen ought to realise that the moment of danger is just when you let down your line. That is the moment when the fish will put up all kinds of games on you, such as rushing at you in a compact mass so fast that you can't take them in, or selecting the largest of their number to snatch away one of your rods.

'We had hardly let down our lines,' says the fisherman, 'when Tom got a perfect monster. That fish would have weighed five pounds – wouldn't it, Tom?'

'Easily,' says Tom.

'Well, Tom started to haul him in and he yelled to Ted and

[99]

me to get the landing net ready and we had him right up to the boat, right up to the very boat' – 'Right up to the boat,' repeated Tom and Edward sadly – 'when the damn line broke and biff! away he went. Say, he must have been two feet long, easily two feet!'

'Did you see him?' asks the young lady who is staying with them. This of course she has no right to ask. It's not a fair question. Among people who go fishing it is ruled out. You may ask if a fish pulled hard, and how much it weighed, but you must not ask whether anybody *saw* the fish.

'We could see where he was,' says Tom.

Then they go on up to the house carrying the 'string' or 'catch' and all three saying at intervals: – 'Say! if we had only landed that big fellow!'

By the time this anecdote has ripened for winter use, the fish will have been drawn actually into the boat (thus settling all question of seeing it), and will there have knocked Edward senseless, and then leaped over the gunwale.

II

STORY OF THE EXTRAORDINARY BAIT

This is a more advanced form of fishing story. It is told by fishermen for fishermen. It is the sort of thing they relate to one another when fishing out of a motor boat on a lake, when there has been a slight pause in their activity and when the fish for a little while – say for two hours – have stopped biting. So the fishermen talk and discuss the ways and means of their craft. Somebody says that grasshoppers make good bait; and somebody else asks whether any of them have ever tried Lake Erie softshell crabs as bait, and then one – whoever is lucky enough to get in first – tells the good old bait story.

'The queerest bait I ever saw used,' he says, shifting his pipe to the other side of his mouth, 'was one day when I was fishing up in one of the lakes back in Maine. We'd got to the spot and got all ready when we suddenly discovered that we'd forgotten the bait—'

At this point any one of the listeners is entitled by custom to put in the old joke about not forgetting the whisky.

'Well, there was no use going ashore. We couldn't have got any worms and it was too early for frogs, and it was ten miles to row back home. We tried chunks of meat from our lunch, but nothing doing! Well, then, just for fun I cut a white bone button off my pants and put it on the hook. Say! you ought to have seen those fish go for it. We caught, oh, easily twenty – yes, thirty – in about half an hour. We only quit after we'd cut off all our buttons and our pants were falling off us! Say, hold on, boys, I believe I've got a nibble! Sit steady!'

Getting a nibble of course will set up an excitement in any fishing party that puts an end to all storytelling. After they have got straight again and the nibble has turned out to be 'the bottom' – as all nibbles are – the moment would be fitting for any one of them to tell the famous story called:

III

**BEGINNER'S LUCK, OR THE WONDERFUL CATCH
MADE BY THE NARRATOR'S WIFE'S LADY
FRIEND**

'Talking of that big catch that you made with the pants button,' says another of the anglers, who really means that he is going to talk of something else, 'reminds me of a queer thing I saw myself. We'd gone out fishing for pickerel, 'Dorés' they call them up there in the lake of Two Mountains. We had a couple of big row boats and we'd taken my wife and the ladies along – I think there were eight of us, or nine perhaps. Anyway, it doesn't matter. Well, there was a young lady there from Dayton, Ohio, and she'd never fished before. In fact she'd never been in a boat before. I don't believe she'd ever been near the water before.'

All experienced listeners know now what is coming. They realize the geographical position of Dayton, Ohio, far from the water and shut in everywhere by land. Any prudent fish would make and sneak for shelter if he knew that a young lady from Dayton, Ohio, was after him.

'Well, this girl got an idea that she'd like to fish and we'd rigged up a line for her just tied on to a cedar pole that we'd cut in the bush. Do you know, you'd hardly believe that girl had hardly got her line into the water when she got a monster. We yelled to her to play it or she'd lose it, but she just heaved it up into the air and right into the boat. She caught seventeen, or twenty-seven, I forget which, one after the other, while the rest of us got nothing. And the fun of it was she didn't know anything about fishing, she just threw the fish up into the air and into the boat. Next day we got her a decent rod with a reel and gave her a lesson or two and then she didn't catch any.'

I may say with truth that I have heard this particular story told not only about a girl from Dayton, Ohio, but about a girl from Kansas, a young lady just out from England, about a girl fresh from Paris, and about another girl, not fresh – the daughter of a minister. In fact, if I wished to make sure of a real catch, I would select a girl fresh from Paris or New York and cut off some of my buttons, or hers, and start to fish.

IV

THE STORY OF WHAT WAS FOUND IN THE FISH

The stories, however, do not end with the mere catching of the fish. There is another familiar line of anecdote that comes in when the fish are to be cleaned and cooked. The fishermen have landed on the rocky shore beside the rushing waterfall and are cleaning their fish to cook them for the midday meal.

There is an obstinate superstition that fish cooked thus taste better than first-class kippered herring put up in a tin in Aberdeen where they know how. They don't, but it is an honourable fiction and reflects credit on humanity. What is more, all the fishing party compete eagerly for the job of cutting the insides out of the dead fish. In a restaurant they are content to leave that to anybody sunk low enough and unhappy enough to have to do it. But in the woods they fight for the job.

So it happens that presently one of the workers holds up some filthy specimen of something in his hand and says, 'Look at that! See what I took out of the trout! Unless I mistake it is part of a deer's ear. The deer must have stooped over the stream to drink and the trout bit his ear off.'

At which somebody – whoever gets it in first – says:

'It's amazing what you find in fish. I remember once trolling for trout, the big trout, up in Lake Simcoe and just off Eight-Mile Point we caught a regular whopper. We had no scales, but he weighed easily twenty pounds. We cut him open on the shore afterwards, and say – would you believe it? – that fish had inside him a brass buckle – the whole of it – and part of a tennis shoe, and a rain-check from a baseball game, and seventy-five cents in change. It seems hard to account for it, unless perhaps he'd been swimming round some summer hotel.'

These stories, I repeat, may now be properly narrated in the summer fishing season. But of course, as all fishermen know, the true time to tell them is round the winter fire, with a glass of something warm within easy reach, at a time when statements cannot be checked, when weights and measures must not be challenged and when fish grow to their full size and their true beauty. It is to such stories as these, whether told in summer or in winter, that the immemorial craft of the angler owes something of its continued charm.

9

A CORNER IN WORMS

by William Caine

Just as Neville Cardus has been described as the greatest modern writer on cricket, and golf has been similarly well served by Bernard Darwin, so the world of fishing has applauded the talents of the next contributor, William Caine. For under his pen-name, 'W. Quilliam' Caine graced the columns of *The Field* magazine for over a quarter of a century, mixing wry humour with a sound knowledge of the sport. Indeed, as a result of this continuing series of essays and short stories he earned himself a large and admiring following among the publication's readers.

Caine's two great pleasures in life were trout fishing and sketching, and often his columns in *The Field* were enlivened by his own light-hearted drawings. When collections of his contributions began appearing in book form, however, he was even more fortunate in securing the services of the great cartoonist, H. M. Bateman – himself a keen angler and author of *The Evening Rise: Fifty Years of Fly Fishing* (1960) – to illustrate these volumes in his own unmistakable style. Among the serious books about the sport which Caine issued were *An Angler at Large* (1911) and *Fish, Fishing and Fisher-men* (1927) while among the collections of his humorous stories two classics are *Fish Tales* (1920) and *What a Scream!* (1927).

Undoubtedly Caine had a large circle of friends in angling circles and he drew on the exploits of some of the more extraordinary of these men as the basis for his comic yarns.

Whether, though, the single-minded fisherman Wynne of this next story, who is so determined to win a sea angling contest, had an original in real life I don't know! But, certainly, while the efforts he makes to secure his victory are absolutely hilarious, they are also surely not so far removed from the stop-at-nothing plans that the occasional fisherman we have all heard of has been guilty of in order to triumph in his chosen sport?

A CORNER IN WORMS

My old friend Wiernershnizel – I should say Wynne, for that is how he prefers nowadays to see his name spelt – is the proprietor of one of the oldest-established and most reputable bucket-shops in Copthall Avenue. There is no shrewder man of business in the City. Never once has Wynne been in jail. I can't tell you how often they have tried to put him there, but he has done them every time. I tell you, he is clever. But it is not with Wynne as a man of business that I am concerned.

He has another side. You will never guess what it is, so I may as well tell you. He is a sportsman to the core of his being. Yes, this astute, rapacious adventurer of the Stock Markets is a sea angler of the most earnest description. Not a Sunday passes from January to December without witnessing the

arrival of my dear old Wynne, loaded with his rods, his pater-
noster, and his bait-cans, upon the point of Brighton, Deal, or
some other pier. He is as indefatigable as he is regular; always
the first angler to arrive, he is ever the last to depart. You
would hardly know Wynne at these times. He is no longer the
keen man of business, with an eye open singly to the main
chance; he is the sportsman, with a soul aflame for the capture
and destruction of dabs, gurnards, and starfish. Business
affairs, though in their way splendid enough, are, after all,
sordid when compared with the things (whatever they may
be) which occupy the thoughts of the sea angler.

That the thoughts of Wynne are not sordid when he is
fishing is pretty conclusively proved by the fact that he never
catches anything at all except, now and then, the girders of a
pier or somebody else's bait. Never yet has he landed a fish.
He is either the most unlucky or most incompetent sea angler
in Great Britain; that is clear. But what I say is, a man who can
go on fishing year after year, winter and summer, rain or shine,
storm or calm, freezing or boiling, with never a fin to show for
it, cannot – I say he cannot – be actuated by motives of gain.
Such a man can be nothing but a sportsman of the very purest
ray. It is obvious.

I hope you won't think that I reflect upon his
sportsmanship when I tell you that Wynne has nearly all his
life cherished the ambition to obtain a prize in an angling
tournament. That doesn't dim his lustre for you, I believe. It
should, on the contrary, brighten it. If it were a mere suitcase
or tantalus that he was after, it might dim him, I admit. But, to
think that, would be to wrong Wynne grievously. He has all
the suitcases and tantaluses he can possibly require. Prizes to
a man like Wynne are symbols merely. They are glory in material form. It has been glory – reputation – that Wynne has been
after all these years.

He wants to be pointed out in Lothbury as the man who, for
example, came out top of thirty thousand at Bexhill, or the
man who broke all the records for Pegwell Bay, or the man

who landed the biggest known codling at Broadstairs in August. That's all he wants. Anyone else may have the barometers and the brandy flasks.

I repeat, the man is a sportsman, through and through.

Now listen to this and tell me if you think there is anything sordid or material about Wynne – Wynne the angler, I mean, of course.

A few months ago the championships of Goodwin's Bay were about to be held, and Wynne (who belongs to every sea angling club in Southeastern England) had entered his name as usual and for every event. Some weeks before the date that had been fixed he had what is at present called a brainstorm. He had just made a hundred and twenty thousand pounds, he and several associates having engineered a highly successful corner in calico. His thoughts were naturally attuned to the engineering of corners. And so while he was furbishing up his tackle one evening for the coming contest at Goodwin's Bay, he suddenly slapped his knee and cried: 'Eureka!' He didn't know what Eureka means; he only knew that it is the proper exclamation with which to hail the birth of a bright idea.

And what was his bright idea?

Nothing less than to go down to Goodwin's Bay, just before the meeting, and corner lug and rag.

What, pray, is lug? What may rag be?

Lug, my poor friend, is an obscene and hairy worm, about as long as your foot, which lurks in the sand and is dug up and dragged out in hundreds by the longshoremen and sold to sea anglers for bait. Rag is another outrage of the same kind. It differs from lug only in the degree of its obscenity. Lug and rag are odious-looking creatures, but the fishes love them, and the sea anglers swear by them, beyond all other baits. In fact, without a large supply of lug and rag no sea angler will approach the ocean with any kind of confidence. To be without lug or rag is, to the sea angler, almost what to be without cartridges is to the gunner, or to be without beer is to the yachtsman.

Do you grasp the significance of Wynne's project now? I hope so. You see – don't you? – that if he could secure all the available supplies of lug and rag for the day of the championships he would be in an almost unassailable position. No one else would have a chance against him.

I maintain, therefore, that for a brainstorm Wynne's brainstorm was something like a brainstorm.

He did this thing. He turned over all the bucket-selling to his partner, went down to Goodwin's Bay three clear days before the date of the competition, and got into touch with the entire bait-digging population of the place. When, on the eve of the contest, he rested from his labours, he had contracts in his pocket covering the entire local harvest of lug and rag for the succeeding twenty-four hours. This, I may tell you, cost him a good deal in earnest money; but what were trouble and money to Wynne when his reputation as a sportsman was concerned? Nothing. Nothing whatever.

You are to know that lug and rag can only be delved out of the sands when the tide is out. You are also to know that the competition was timed to last from 10.30 a.m. to 4.30 p.m., when there would be water under the whole length of the pier, and, consequently, over those sands where dwell the worms aforesaid. Of all this Wynne was well aware; indeed, his whole scheme depended on it. He was quite certain of his ground, because these tidal arrangements are not accidental. The officials of Trinity House decide them in consultation with the editor of Whitaker's Almanack and the secretary of the British Sea Anglers' Association. Oh! Wynne knew exactly what he was doing.

Day dawned upon the backs of a hundred and fifty long-shoremen howking out the lug and rag from their holes. When the tide flowed and interrupted their labours the number of the worms which were held at Wynne's sole disposal staggers belief and imagination.

Wynne, furnished with a large bag of coin, stood at the foot of the pier; one by one the longshoremen brought him their treasure and poured it out of buckets into the bait-cans with which Wynne had surrounded himself. At last the final lug was delivered up, the ultimate rag exchanged for copper.

Wynne, owner of every sandworm in Goodwin's Bay, stood, master of the situation, to await the arrival of the sea anglers. Their train was due in at 10.12.

As for the longshoremen, having nothing more to do at the pier, these persons betook themselves to the drinking houses of Goodwin's Bay.

The 10.12 arrived, the sea anglers precipitated themselves out of the station and ran furiously to the pier, feeling in their pockets for money wherewith to purchase bait. They made no doubt, the unsuspecting wretches, that they would, as always upon this great day of the Goodwin's Bay year, be greeted with the lusty cry, from a hundred and fifty longshore throats, of, 'Fine lug, gentlemen, good rag, gentlemen! Six a penny! Good lug! Fine rag! Thirdeen fer tuppence!'

To their stupefaction there was not a single worm-merchant in sight. Only Wynne, the centre of bait-cans, stood by the turnstiles, hellishly smiling.

The sea anglers halted in a body, questioning with large eyes the meaning of this sinister spectacle. Then suddenly they realised what had happened (for sea anglers have brains, I may tell you), and at once they were again in motion, charging down upon Wynne with shouts of 'How much the lug? What price the rag?'

Wynne waved them away and held up his hand for silence. 'No price the lug,' he said. 'The rag is not for sale.'

A scream of anguish arose. Poor devils! they knew Wynne's City reputation, and they understood that they were up against it. They wasted no time in supplication, but began instantly to bid against one another for the bait.

'I'll give you sixpence a dozen!' they shouted. 'I'll give a shilling. Two shillings. Half a crown. Five bob.'

Now this is where the proof of Wynne's perfect sportsmanship appears. He had these men at his mercy. They were crazy for the lug and the rag, without which their angling must be a mockery. They were losing their heads all round him, offering shillings for penn'orths, bidding crowns for what had cost him but a copper or two. Yet he held to his purpose. He kept his vision. He stuck to his worms.

After that I imagine that you won't be inclined to think that there was very much sordidness about Wynne – I mean always Wynne the angler.

Presently the sea anglers understood that they were losing their time with Wynne. They began to scatter in search of longshoremen. The longshoremen were already beginning to straggle, refreshed, out of those places into which they had lately vanished. The sea anglers prostrated themselves before those longshoremen and begged for worms at any price. In vain.

Worms in Goodwin's Bay were 'off' until the tide should recede. And by that time the competition would have been fought out. Well, I don't want to linger over the sorrows of these poor men, and I don't want unduly to prolong this history. I was, after all, only concerned to show you how sportsmanship can ennoble a man, how it can purge him of all desire for material gain. I suppose Wynne could have made as much as two pounds ten, or perhaps even three pounds profit, if he had listened to the promptings of his mercantile instincts. He bade them be silent. He gave up gold for glory. Well, I say that was a fine thing, finely done. That's all. I only say that.

The pity is that Wynne should have got nothing out of it. He deserved better fortune. The fact remains that, for all his worms, he never caught a thing all day but a pair of old trousers. Awful old trousers they were, obviously discarded by a longshoreman, and a longshoreman, as is well known, has to be practically arrestable before he discards his trousers.

Yes, that's all that Wynne fished out of the sea, and with only a pair of trousers to show he could qualify for none of the prizes. Whereas (for no other sea angler, naturally, caught so much as a button) if he had managed to secure even a pale green crab he would have won every prize there was – for the greatest number of fishes, greatest aggregate weight, greatest average, heaviest single fish, and fish in best condition, as well as all the booby prizes for the smallest number, smallest aggregate weight, smallest average, lightest fish, shortest fish, and worst-conditioned fish. But it was not to be.

However, he has the consolation that he acted like a true sportsman. Of that Wynne is not to be robbed. And he is able, at any rate, to be pointed out in Threadneedle Street as the man who cornered worms.

That is, in a way, a distinction.

10

THE RIVER GOD

by Roland Pertwee

ROLAND PERTWEE was for many years a leading English play-wright, novelist and short story writer – and also the father of actor, Jon Pertwee, famous for his radio characterisations and TV appearances as Doctor Who and Worzel Gummidge. Jon has recalled that his father was a dedicated fisherman all his life and did his best to pass this enthusiasm on to his son – though with a singular lack of success for the actor admits he prefers to spend his spare time in such hectic activities as riding motorcycles or piloting high speed motorboats!

The older Pertwee's love of angling can be discovered in several of his books, including the highly amusing *Fish Are Such Liars!* (1931) and *May We Come Through?* (1940). The title story of the first collection has been anthologised several times, and funny as it is I have resisted the temptation to include it here yet again. Instead, I have selected a tale which has not appeared in any of Roland Pertwee's books called, 'The River God'. Written for the prestigious American maga-zine, *The Saturday Evening Post* in July 1928, it is a nostalgic and at times very amusing story about a young boy's discovery of the joys of fishing under the guidances of an older man – and it is not difficult to believe that there are probably a number of the author's own experiences in the fine piece of writing which follows . . .

THE RIVER GOD

When I was a little boy I had a friend who was a colonel. He was not the kind of colonel you meet nowadays, who manages a motor showroom in the West End of London and wears crocodile shoes and a small moustache and who calls you 'old man' and slaps your back, independent of the fact that you may have been no more than a private in the war. My colonel was of the older order that takes a third of a century and a lot of Indian sun and Madras curry in the making.

A veteran of the Mutiny he was, and wore side whiskers to prove it.

Once he came upon a number of sepoys conspiring mis-chief in a byre with a barrel of gunpowder. So he put the butt of his cheroot into the barrel and presently they all went to hell. That was the kind of man he was in the way of business.

In the way of pleasure he was very different. In the way of pleasure he wore an old Norfolk coat that smelt of heather and brine, and which had no elbows to speak of. And he wore a Sherlock Holmesy kind of cap with a swarm of salmon flies upon it, that to my boyish fancy was more splendid than a crown. I cannot remember his legs, because they were nearly always under water, hidden in great canvas waders. But once he sent me a photograph of himself riding on a tricycle, so I expect he had some knickerbockers too, which would have been that tight kind, with box cloth under the knees.

Boys don't take much stock of clothes. His head occupied my imagination. A big, brave, white-haired head with cherry-red rugose cheeks and honest, laughing, puckered eyes, with gunpowder marks in their corners.

People at the little Welsh fishing inn where we met said he was a bore; but I knew him to be a god and shall prove it.

I was ten years old and his best friend.

He was seventy something and my hero.

Properly I should not have mentioned my hero so soon in this narrative. He belongs to a later epoch, but sometimes it is forgivable to start with a boast, and now that I have com-mitted myself I lack the courage to call upon my colonel to fall back two paces to the rear, quick march, and wait until he is wanted.

The real beginning takes place, as I remember, somewhere in Hampshire on the Grayshott Road, among sandy banks, sentinel firs, and plum-coloured wastes of heather. Summer holiday time it was, and I was among folks whose names have since vanished like lizards under the stones of forgetfulness.

Perhaps it was a picnic walk; perhaps I carried a basket and was told not to swing it for fear of bursting its cargo of ginger beer. In those days ginger beer had big bulgy corks held down with string. In a hot sun or under stress of too much agitation the string would break and the corks fly. Then there would be a merry foaming fountain and someone would get reproached.

One of our company had a fishing rod. He was a young man who, one day, was to be an uncle of mine. But that didn't concern me. What concerned me was the fishing rod, and presently – perhaps because he felt he must keep in with the family – he let me carry it.

To the fisherman born there is nothing so provoking of curiosity as a fishing rod in a case. Surreptitiously I opened the flap, which contained a small brass spear in a wee pocket, and, pulling down the case a little, I admired the beauties of the cork butt, with its gunmetal ferrule and reel rings and the exquisite frail slenderness of two top joints.

'It's got two top joints – two!' I exclaimed ecstatically.

'Of course,' said he. 'All good trout rods have two.'

I marvelled in silence at what seemed to me then a combination of extravagance and excellent precaution.

There must have been something inherently understanding and noble about that young man who would one day be my uncle, for, taking me by the arm, he sat me down on a tuft of heather and took the pieces of rod from the case and fitted them together.

The rest of the company moved on and left me in paradise.

It is thirty-five years ago since that moment and not one detail of it is forgotten. There sounds in my ears today as clearly as then the faint, clear pop made by the little cork stoppers with their boxwood tops as they were withdrawn. I remember how, before fitting the pieces together, he rubbed the ferrules against the side of his nose to prevent them sticking. I remember looking up the length of it through a tunnel of sneck rings to the eyelet at the end. Not until he had fixed a reel and passed a line through the rings did he put the lovely thing into my hand.

So light it was, so firm, so persuasive; such a thing alive – a sceptre. I could do no more than say 'Oo!' and again, 'Oo!'

'A thrill, ain't it?' said he.

I had no need to answer that. In my new-found rapture was only one sorrow – the knowledge that such happiness would not endure, and that, all too soon, a blank and rodless future awaited me.

'They must be awfully – awfully 'spensive,' I said.

'Couple of guineas,' he replied off-handedly.

A couple of guineas! And we were poor folk and the future was more rodless than ever.

'Then I shall save and save and save,' I said.

And my imagination started to add up twopence a week into guineas. Two hundred and forty pennies to the pound, multiplied by two – four hundred and eighty – and then another twenty-four pennies – five hundred and four. Why, it would take a lifetime, and no sweets, no elastic for catapults, no penny novelty boxes or air gun bullets or ices or anything.

Tragedy must have been writ large upon my face, for he said suddenly, 'When's your birthday?'

I was almost ashamed to tell him how soon it was. Perhaps he, too, was a little taken aback by its proximity, for that future uncle of mine was not so rich as uncles should be.

'We must see about it.'

'But it wouldn't – it couldn't be one like that,' I said.

I must have touched his pride, for he answered loftily, 'Certainly it will.'

In the fortnight that followed I walked on air and told everybody I had as 'good as got a couple-of-guineas rod'.

No one can deceive a child, save the child himself, and when my birthday came and with it a long brown paper parcel, I knew, even before I had removed the wrappers, that this two-guinea rod was not worth the money. There was a brown linen case, it is true, but it was not a case with a neat compartment for each joint, nor was there a spear in the flap. There was only one top instead of two, and there were no

[119]

popping little stoppers to protect the ferrules from dust and injury. The lower joint boasted no elegant cork hand piece, but was a tapered affair coarsely made and rudely varnished.

When I fitted the pieces together, what I balanced in my hand was tough and stodgy rather than limber. The reel, which had come in a different parcel, was of wood. It had neither check nor brake, and the line overran and back-wound itself with distressing frequency.

I had not read and reread Gamages' price list without knowing something of rods, and I did not need to look long at this rod before realising that it was no match to the one I had handled on the Grayshott Road.

I believe at first a great sadness possessed me, but very presently imagination came to the rescue. For I told myself that I had only to think that this was the rod of all other rods that I desired most and it would be so. And it was so.

Furthermore, I told myself that, in this great wide, ignorant world, but few people existed with such expert knowledge of rods as I possessed. That I had but to say, 'Here is the final word in good rods,' and they would accept it as such.

Very confidently I tried the experiment on my mother, with inevitable success. From the depths of her affection and her ignorance on all such matters she produced:

'It's a magnificent rod.'

I went my way, knowing full well that she knew not what she said, but that she was kind.

With rather less confidence I approached my father, saying, 'Look, father! It cost two guineas. It's absolutely the best sort you can get.'

And he, after waggling it a few moments in silence, quoted cryptically:

'There is nothing either good or bad, but thinking makes it so.'

Young as I was, I had some curiosity about words, and on any other occasion I would have called on him to explain. But this I did not do, but left hurriedly, for fear that he should explain.

*

In the two years that followed, I fished every day in the slip of a back garden of our tiny London house. And, having regard to the fact that this rod was never fashioned to throw a fly, I acquired a pretty knack in the fullness of time and performed some glib casting at the nasturtiums and marigolds that flourished by the back wall.

My parents' fortunes must have been in the ascendant, I suppose, for I call to mind an unforgettable breakfast when my mother told me that father had decided we should spend our summer holiday at a Welsh hotel on the river Lledr. The place was called Pont-y-pant, and she showed me a picture of the hotel with a great knock-me-down river creaming past the front of it.

Although in my dreams I had heard fast water often enough, I had never seen it, and the knowledge that in a month's time I should wake with the music of a cataract in my ears was almost more than patience could endure.

In that exquisite, intolerable period of suspense I suffered as only childish longing and enthusiasm can suffer. Even the hank of gut that I bought and bent into innumerable casts failed to alleviate that suffering. I would walk for miles for a moment's delight captured in gluing my nose to the windows of tackleists' shops in the West End.

I learned from my grandmother – a wise and calm old lady – how to make nets and, having mastered the art, I made myself a landing net. This I set up on a frame fashioned from a penny schoolmaster's cane bound to an old walking stick. It would be pleasant to record that this was a good and serviceable net, but it was not. It flopped over in a very distressing fashion when called upon to lift the lightest weight. I had to confess to myself that I had more enthusiasm than skill in the manufacture of such articles.

At school there was a boy who had a fishing creel, which he swapped with me for a Swedish knife, a copy of *Rogues of the Fiery Cross*, and an Easter egg which I had kept on account of its rare beauty.

He had forced a hard bargain and was sure he had the best of it, but I knew otherwise.

At last the great day dawned, and after infinite travel by train we reached our destination as the glow of sunset was greying into dark. The river was in spate, and as we crossed a tall stone bridge on our way to the hotel I heard it below me, barking and grumbling among great rocks. I was pretty far gone in tiredness, for I remember little else that night but a rod rack in the hall – a dozen rods of different sorts and sizes, with gaudy salmon flies, some nets, a gaff, and an oak coffer upon which lay a freshly caught salmon on a blue ashet. Then supper by candlelight, bed, a glitter of stars through the open window, and the ceaseless drumming of water.

By six o'clock next morning I was on the river bank, fitting my rod together and watching in awe the great brown ribbon of water go fleetly by.

Among my most treasured possessions were half a dozen flies, and two of these I attached to the cast with exquisite care. While so engaged, a shadow fell on the grass beside me and, looking up, I beheld a lank, shabby individual with a walrus moustache and an unhealthy face, who, the night before, had helped with our luggage at the station.

'Water's too heavy for flies,' said he, with an uptilting inflection. 'This evening, yes; now, no – none whateffer. Better try with a worrum in the burrun.'

He pointed at a busy little brook which tumbled down the steep hillside and joined the main stream at the garden end.

'C-couldn't I fish with a fly in the – burrun?' I asked, for although I wanted to catch a fish very badly, for honour's sake I would fain take it on a fly.

'Indeed, no,' he replied, slanting the tone of his voice skyward. 'You cootn't. Neffer. And that isn't a fly rod whateffer.'

'It is,' I replied hotly. 'Yes, it is.'

But he only shook his head and repeated, 'No,' and took the

rod from my hand and illustrated its awkwardness and handed it back with a wretched laugh.

If he had pitched me into the river I should have been happier.

'It is a fly rod and it cost two guineas,' I said, and my lower lip trembled.

'Neffer,' he repeated. 'Five shillings would be too much.'

Even a small boy is entitled to some dignity.

Picking up my basket, I turned without another word and made for the hotel. Perhaps my eyes were blinded with tears, for I was about to plunge into the dark hall when a great, rough, kindly voice arrested me with:

'Easy does it.'

At the thick end of an immense salmon rod there strode out into the sunlight the noblest figure I had ever seen.

There is no real need to describe my colonel again – I have done so already – but the temptation is too great. Standing in the doorway, the sixteen-foot rod in hand, the deerstalker hat, besprent with flies, crowning his shaggy head, the waders, like sevenleague boots, braced up to his armpits, the creel across his shoulder, a gaff across his back, he looked what he was – a god. His eyes met mine with that kind of smile one good man keeps for another.

'An early start,' he said. 'Any luck, old fellar?'

I told him I hadn't started – not yet.

'Wise chap,' said he. 'Water's a bit heavy for trouting. It'll soon run down through. Let's vet those flies of yours.'

He took my rod and whipped it expertly.

'A nice piece – new, eh?'

'N-not quite,' I stammered; 'but I haven't used it yet, sir, in water.'

That god read men's minds.

'I know – garden practice; capital; nothing like it.'

Releasing my cast, he frowned critically over the flies – a Blue Dun and a March Brown.

'Think so?' he queried. 'You don't think it's a shade late in the season for these fancies?' I said I thought perhaps it was. 'Yes, I think you're right,' said he. 'I believe in this big water you'd do better with a livelier pattern. Teal and Red, Cock-y-bundy, Greenwell's Glory.'

I said nothing, but nodded gravely at these brave names.

Once more he read my thoughts and saw through the wicker sides of my creel a great emptiness.

'I expect you've fished most in southern rivers. These Welsh trout have a fancy for a spot of colour.'

He rummaged in the pocket of his Norfolk jacket and produced a round tin which once had held saddle soap.

'Collar on to that,' said he; 'there's a proper pickle of flies and casts in that tin that, as a keen fisherman, you won't mind sorting out. Still, they may come in useful.'

'But, I say, you don't mean—' I began.

'Yes, go on; stick to it. All fishermen are members of the same club, and I'm giving the trout a rest for a bit.' His eyes ranged the hills and trees opposite. 'I must be getting on with it before the sun's too high.'

Waving his free hand, he strode away and presently was lost to view at a bend in the road.

I think my mother was a little piqued by my abstraction during breakfast. My eyes never for an instant deserted the round tin box which lay open beside my plate. Within it were a paradise and a hundred miracles all tangled together in the pleasantest disorder. My mother said something about a lovely walk over the hills, but I had other plans, which included a very glorious hour which should be spent untangling and wrapping up in neat squares of paper my new treasures.

'I suppose he knows best what he wants to do,' she said.

So it came about that I was left alone, and betook myself to a sheltered spot behind a rock where all the delicious disorder was remedied and I could take stock of what was mine.

I am sure there were at least six casts all set up with flies, and ever so many loose flies and one great stout, tapered cast, with a salmon fly upon it, that was so rich in splendour that I doubted if my benefactor could really have known that it was there.

I felt almost guilty at owning so much, and not until I had done full justice to everything did I fasten a new cast to my line and go a-fishing.

There is a lot said and written about beginner's luck, but none of it came my way. Indeed, I spent most of the morning extricating my line from the most fearsome tangles. I had no skill in throwing a cast with two droppers upon it and I found it was an art not to be learned in a minute.

Then, from overeagerness, I was too snappy with my back cast, whereby before many minutes had gone I heard that warning crack behind me that betokens the loss of a tail fly. I must have spent half an hour searching the meadow for that lost fly and finding it not. Which is not strange, for I wonder has any fisherman ever found that lost fly. The reeds, the buttercups, and the little people with many legs who run in the wet grass conspire together to keep the secret of its hiding place.

I gave up at last, and with a feeling of shame that was only proper, I invested a new fly on the point of my cast and set to work again, but more warily.

In that hard racing water a good strain was put upon my rod, and before the morning was out it was creaking at the joints in a way that kept my heart continually in my mouth. It is the duty of a rod to work with a single smooth action and by no means to divide its performance into three sections of activity. It is a hard task for any angler to persuade his line austerely if his rod behaves thus.

When, at last, my father strolled up the river bank, walking, to his shame, much nearer the water than a good fisherman should, my nerves were jumpy from apprehension.

'Come along. Food's ready. Done any good?' he said.

Again it was to his discredit that he put food before sport, but I told him I had had a wonderful morning, and he was glad.

'What do you want to do this afternoon, old man?' he asked.

'Fish,' I said.

'But you can't always fish,' he said.

I told him I could, and I was right, and have proved it for thirty years and more.

'Well, well,' he said, 'please yourself, but isn't it dull not catching anything?'

And I said, as I've said a thousand times since, 'As if it could be.'

So that afternoon I went downstream instead of up, and found myself in difficult country where the river boiled between the narrows of two hills. Stunted oaks overhung the water and great boulders opposed its flow. Presently I came to a sort of natural flight of steps – a pool and a cascade three times repeated – and there, watching the maniac fury of the waters in awe and wonderment, I saw the most stirring sight in my young life.

I saw a silver salmon leap superbly from the cauldron below into the pool above. And I saw another and another salmon do likewise. And I wonder the eyes of me did not fall out of my head.

I cannot say how long I stayed watching that gallant pageant of leaping fish – in ecstasy there is no measurement of time – but at last it came upon me that all the salmon in the sea were careering past me and that if I were to realise my soul's desire I must hasten to the pool below before the last of them had gone by.

It was a mad adventure, for until I had discovered that stout cast, with the gaudy fly attached in the tin box, I had given no thought to such noble quarry. My recent possessions had put ideas into my head above my station and beyond my powers. Failure, however, means little to the young, and, walking fast,

yet gingerly, for fear of of breaking my rod top against a tree, I
followed the path downstream until I came to a great basin of
water into which, through a narrow throat, the river
thundered like a storm.

At the head of the pool was a plate of rock scored by the
nails of fishermen's boots, and here I sat me down to wait
while the salmon cast, removed from its wrapper, was allowed
to soak and soften in a puddle left by the rain.

And while I waited a salmon rolled not ten yards from
where I sat. Head and tail, up and down he went, a great
monster of a fish, sporting and deriding me.

With that performance so near at hand, I have often wondered how I was able to control my fingers well enough to tie a
figure-eight knot between the line and the cast. But I did, and
I'm proud to be able to record it. Your true-born angler does
not go blindly to work until he has first satisfied his conscience. There is a pride, in knots, of which the laity knows
nothing, and if, through neglect to tie them rightly, failure and
loss should result pride may not be restored nor conscience
salved by the plea of eagerness.

With my trembling fingers I bent the knot, and with a
pummelling heart, launched the line into the broken water at
the throat of the pool.

At first the mere tug of the water against that large fly was so
thrilling to me that it was hard to believe that I had not hooked
a whale. The trembling line swung round in a wide arc into a
calm eddy below where I stood. Before casting afresh I shot a
glance over my shoulder to assure myself there was no limb of
a tree behind me to foul the fly. And this was a gallant cast,
true and straight, with a couple of yards more length than its
predecessor, and a wide radius. Instinctively I knew, as if the
surface had been marked with an × where the salmon had
risen, that my fly must pass right over the spot. As it swung by,
my nerves were strained like piano wires. I think I knew that
something tremendous, impossible, terrifying was going to

happen. The sense, the certitude was so strong in me that I half opened my mouth to shout a warning to the monster, not to.

I must have felt very, very young in that moment. I, who that same day had been talked to as a man by a man among men. The years were stripped from me and I was what I was – ten years old and appalled.

And then, with the suddenness of a rocket, it happened. The water was cut into a swathe. I remember a silver loop bearing downwards – a bright, shining, vanishing thing like the bobbin of my mother's sewing machine – and a tug. I shall never forget the viciousness of that tug. I had my fingers tight upon the line, so I got the full force of it. To counteract a tendency to go head first into the spinning water below, I threw myself backward and sat down on the hard rock with a jar that shut my teeth on my tongue – like the jaws of a trap.

Luckily I had let the rod go out straight with the line, else it must have snapped in the first frenzy of the down stream rush. Little ass that I was, I tried to check the speeding line with my forefinger, with the result that it cut and burnt me to the bone. There wasn't above twenty yards of line in the reel, and the wretched contrivance was trying to be rid of the line even faster than the fish was wrenching it out.

Heaven knows why it didn't snarl, for great loops and whorls were whirling, like Catherine wheels, under my wrist. An instant's glance revealed the terrifying fact that there were not more than half a dozen yards left on the reel, and the fish showed no sign of abating his rush. With the realisation of impending and inevitable catastrophe upon me, I launched a yell for help, which, rising above the roar of the waters, went echoing down the gorge.

And then, to add to my terrors, the salmon leaped – a swinging leap like a silver arch appearing and instantly disappearing upon the broken surface. So mighty, so all-powerful he seemed in that sublime moment that I lost all sense of reason and raised the rod, with a sudden jerk, above my head.

I have often wondered, had the rod actually been the two-guinea rod my imagination claimed for it, whether it could have withstood the strain thus violently and unreasonably imposed upon it. The wretched thing that I held so grimly never even put up a fight. It snapped at the ferrule of the lower joint and plunged like a toboggan down the slanting line, to vanish into the black depths of the water.

My horror at this calamity was so profound that I was lost even to the consciousness that the last of my line had run out. A couple of vicious tugs advised me of this awful truth. Then, snap! The line parted at the reel, flickered out through the rings, and was gone. I was left with nothing but the butt of a broken rod in my hand, and an agony of mind that even now I cannot recall without emotion.

I am not ashamed to confess that I cried. I lay down on the rock with my cheek in the puddle where I had soaked the cast, and plenished it with my tears. For what had the future left for me but a cut and burning finger, a badly bumped behind, the single joint of a broken rod, and no faith in uncles?

How long I lay there weeping I do not know. Ages, perhaps, or minutes, or seconds.

I was roused by a rough hand on my shoulder, and a kindly voice demanding, 'Hurt yourself, Ike Walton?'

Blinking away my tears, I pointed at my broken rod with a bleeding forefinger.

'Come! This is bad luck,' said my colonel, his face grave as a stone. 'How did it happen?'

'I c-caught a s-salmon.'

'You what?' he said.

'I d-did,' I said.

He looked at me long and earnestly; then, taking my injured hand, he looked at that and nodded.

'The poor groundlings who can find no better use for a river than something to put a bridge over think all fishermen are liars,' said he. 'But we know better, eh? By the bumps and

[129]

breaks and cuts I'd say you made a plucky fight against heavy odds. Let's hear all about it.'

So, with his arm round my shoulders and his great shaggy head near to mine, I told him all about it.

At the end he gave me a mighty and comforting squeeze, and he said, 'The loss of one's first big fish is the heaviest loss I know. One feels, whatever happens, one'll never—' He stopped and pointed dramatically. 'There it goes – see! Down there at the tail of the pool!'

In the broken water where the pool emptied itself into the shallows beyond I saw the top joints of my rod dancing on the surface.

'Come on!' he shouted, and gripping my hand, jerked me to my feet. 'Scatter your legs! There's just a chance!'

Dragging me after him, we raced along by the river path to the end of the pool, where, on a narrow promontory of grass, his enormous salmon rod was lying.

'Now,' he said, picking it up and making the line whistle to and fro in the air with sublime authority, 'keep your eyes skinned on those shallows for another glimpse of it.'

A second later I was shouting, 'There! There!'

He must have seen the rod point at the same moment, for his line flowed out and the big fly hit the water with a plop not a couple of feet from the spot.

He let it ride on the current, playing it with a sensitive touch like the brushwork of an artist.

'Half a jiffy!' he exclaimed at last. 'Wait! Yes, I think so. Cut down to that rock and see if I haven't fished up the line.'

I needed no second invitation and presently was yelling, 'Yes – yes, you have!'

'Stretch yourself out then and collar hold of it.'

With the most exquisite care he navigated the line to where I lay stretched upon the rock. Then:

'Right you are! Good lad! I'm coming down.'

Considering his age, he leaped the rocks like a chamois.

'Now,' he said, and took the wet line delicately between his forefinger and thumb. One end trailed limply downstream, but the other end seemed anchored in the big pool where I had had my unequal and disastrous contest.

Looking into his face, I saw a sudden light of excitement dancing in his eyes.

'Odd,' he muttered, 'but not impossible.'

'What isn't?' I asked breathlessly.

'Well, it looks to me as if the top joints of that rod of yours have gone downstream.'

Gingerly he pulled up the line, and presently an end with a broken knot appeared.

'The reel knot, eh?' I nodded gloomily. 'Then we lose the rod,' said he. That wasn't very heartening news. 'On the other hand, it's just possible the fish is still on – sulking.'

'Oo!' I exclaimed.

'Now, steady does it,' he warned, 'and give me my rod.'

Taking a pair of clippers from his pocket, he cut his own line just above the cast.

'Can you tie a knot?' he asked.

'Yes,' I nodded.

'Come on then; bend your line on to mine. Quick as lightning.'

Under his critical eye I joined the two lines with a blood knot. 'I guessed you were a fisherman,' he said, nodded approvingly, and clipped off the ends. 'And now to know the best or the worst.'

I shall never forget the music of that check reel or the suspense with which I watched as, with the butt of the rod bearing against the hollow of his thigh, he steadily wound up the wet slack line. Every instant I expected it to come drifting downstream, but it didn't. Presently it rose in a tight slant from the pool above.

'Snagged, I'm afraid,' he said, and worked the rod with an easy straining motion to and fro. 'Yes, I'm afraid – no, by Lord Bobs, he's on!'

I think it was only right and proper that I should have launched a yell of triumph as, with the spoken word, the point at which the line cut the water shifted magically from the left side of the pool to the right.

'And a fish too,' said he.

In the fifteen minutes that followed, I must have experienced every known form of terror and delight.

'Youngster,' said he, 'you should be doing this by rights, but I'm afraid the rod's a bit above your weight.'

'Oh, go on and catch him,' I pleaded.

'And so I will,' he promised; 'unship the gaff, young un, and stand by to use it, and if you break the cast we'll never speak to each other again, and that's a bet.'

But I didn't break the cast. The noble, courageous, indomitable example of my river god had lent me skill and precision beyond my years. When at long last a weary, beaten, silver monster rolled within reach of my arm into a shallow eddy, the steel gaff shot out fair and true and sank home.

And then I was lying on the grass, with my arms round a salmon that weighed twenty-two pounds on the scale and contained every sort of happiness known to a boy.

And best of all, my river god shook hands with me and called me 'partner'.

That evening the salmon was placed upon the blue ashet in the hall, bearing a little card with its weight and my name upon it.

And I am afraid I sat on a chair facing it for ever so long, so that I could hear what the other anglers had to say as they passed by. I was sitting there when my colonel put his head out of his private sitting-room and beckoned me in.

'A true fisherman lives in the future, not the past, old man,' said he; 'though, for this once, it 'ud be a shame to reproach you.'

'We got the fish,' said he, 'but we lost the rod, and the future without a rod doesn't bear thinking of. Now' – and he pointed at a long wooden box on the floor, that overflowed with rods of different sorts and sizes – 'rummage among those. Take your time and see if you can find anything to suit you.'

'Oo, sir,' I said.

'Here, quit that,' he ordered gruffly. 'By Lord Bobs, if a show like this afternoon's don't deserve a medal, what does? Now, here's a handy piece by Hardy – a light and useful tool – or if you fancy greenheart in preference to split bamboo—'

I have the rod to this day, and I count it among my dearest treasures. And to this day I have a flick of the wrist that was his legacy. I have, too, some small skill in dressing flies, the elements of which were learned in his company by candlelight after the day's work was over. And I have countless memories of that month-long, month-short friendship – the closest and most perfect friendship, perhaps, of all my life.

He came to the station and saw me off.

How I vividly remember his shaggy head at the window, with the whiskered cheeks and the gunpowder marks at the corners of his eyes! I didn't cry, although I wanted to awfully. We were partners and shook hands. I never saw him again, although on my birthdays I would have coloured cards from him, with Irish, Scotch, Norwegian postmarks. Very brief they were: 'Water very low.' 'Took a good fish last Thursday.' 'Been prawning, but don't like it.'

Sometimes at Christmas I had gifts – a reel, a tapered line, a fly book. But I never saw him again.

Came at last no more postcards or gifts, but in the *Fishing Gazette*, of which I was a religious reader, was an obituary telling how one of the last of the Mutiny veterans had joined the great majority. It seems he had been fishing half an hour before he died.

So he was no more – my river god – and what was left to him they had put into a box and buried it in the earth.

But that isn't true; nor is it true that I never saw him again. For I seldom go a-fishing but that I meet him on the river banks.

The banks of a river are frequented by a strange company

and are full of mysterious and murmurous sounds – the cluck and laughter of water, the piping of birds, the hum of insects, and the whispering of wind in the willows. What should prevent a man in such a place having a word and speech with another who is not there? So much of fishing lies in imagination, and mine needs little stretching to give my river god a living form.

'With this ripple,' says he, 'you should do well.'

'And what's it to be,' say I – 'Blue Upright, Red Spinner? What's your fancy, sir?'

Spirits never grow old. He has begun to take an interest in dry fly methods – that river god of mine, with his seven-league boots, his shaggy head, and the gaff across his back.

11

AN UNLIKELY HAUL

by Lord Dunsany

IRISH-BORN Lord Dunsany was an archetypal 'huntin', shootin' and fishin'' nobleman who was also a master with words and has been described as one of the great fantasy fiction writers of this century. He was the 18th Baron of an ancient Irish family, the Plunketts, and after being educated at Eton and Sandhurst served with the Inniskilling Fusiliers during World War One. Thereafter he became a leading novelist, poet and playwright, based primarily in London, though he frequently returned to Ireland to pursue his great love of outdoor sports.

Lord Dunsany was a big, bluff man with a bubbling sense of fun and a penchant for playing practical jokes. He also loved inventing tall stories, and in fact wrote a whole string of such yarns about a witty and somewhat larger-than-life character named Joseph Jorkens who is forever amazing and amusing fellow members of the Billiards Club in London with outlandish stories. He is usually persuaded to tell these tales in order to win bets or secure himself some free drinks. A good many of Jorkens' stories feature their creator's love of hunting, shooting and fishing and the best of these yarns have been collected in volumes such as *The Travel Tales of Mr. Joseph Jorkens* (1931) *Jorkens Has A Large Whiskey* (1940) and *Jorkens Borrows Another Whiskey* (1954). One of my favourites among Jorkens' tales is the following story about fishing which I suspect the reader will greet with the same mixture of surprise and bewilderment as the members of the Billiards Club . . .

AN UNLIKELY HAUL

There is a certain attitude taken by some at the Billiards Club towards my friend Jorkens, which I hope has not spread beyond its walls. If I were to express that attitude in a single word, the word would be Doubt. Whether any who have read some of the tales that I have recorded from time to time as I heard them from Jorkens may have felt any doubts of them I do not know, but I set down this tale not entirely for any slight interest it may possess for those interested in wells and the various objects their waters may be sometimes found to contain; but I more particularly record it because I know the tale to be true, being acquainted with one of the men to whom it occurred, and able thereby to check Jorkens' veracity, who was there as a chance onlooker, but a perfectly accurate one.

'I was taking a walk in India,' Jorkens began.

'What for?' asked Terbut.

'To get away from the flies,' said Jorkens.

'How far did you have to go to do that?' asked Terbut.

'Three thousand miles,' said Jorkens. 'But why not start? In fact I felt I couldn't delay any longer. Perhaps you don't know those flies?'

Terbut shook his head rather impatiently; for we all knew, and Jorkens better than most of us, that Terbut had never travelled.

'Well,' Jorkens continued, 'I was walking over a plain with a good deal of grass on it, and it was hot enough to kill more than grass, and there was nothing to see on it except a horse grazing, if nibbling that withered stuff can be so described; and he was grazing with a bit in his mouth and a saddle on his back. And then I came suddenly on a well. A rather thick patch of grass hid it entirely, until I was right on top of it. And when I did get there I saw a little flight of steps, cut out of the dry mud of which all that part of the world seems to be made, going down to the well. And on one of the lower steps a man was seated, holding a rod. I never saw him till I stood at the top step, and he didn't see me even then, being so intent on the water.

'"Fishing?"' I said.

'"It's a spear,"' he answered, and sat there patiently for a few more seconds, leaning over the water not looking at me, then made a jab. There was some commotion in the well, in fact more noise than I ever heard in any well before, and then he made another jab; and this time, above the noise of the threshing of water, I clearly heard a pig squeal.

'"Have you got a pig in the well?"' I asked.

'"Sounds like it,"' he said.

When the pig stopped squealing he leaned forward and began to pull; and very soon he hauled up a man out of the well, but the noise of some big thing swimming did not stop. It turned out from their conversation to each other, though they said little enough to me, that the second man had been hanging by one arm from the lower step of the well, the other arm being broken. The noise in the well continued, and rather puzzled me.

'"Have you got anything more down there?"' I asked them.

'"Only a horse,"' said the one that I had mistaken for a fisherman. And he went on with his angling, until he got a pair of reins on the end of his spear. And sure enough there was a horse at the end of the reins, just as the man had said. I admit I hadn't believed him all at once, and perhaps it is rather a lesson to us not to disbelieve a thing merely because it's unlikely; and a horse in a well seemed so very unlikely, especially a well that already had so much else in it. But I was wrong, for very soon I saw a horse's head appearing; and more than that the two men could not manage to bring to sight for a long time.'

'But what was it all about?' asked Terbut. 'What were they doing?'

'They told me that,' said Jorkens. 'They were a long while getting the horse out, and every now and then one of them would call out to me a few words of explanation: you couldn't call it a story, just explanation. And what I gathered from it all was that they had been out pig-sticking and they had come on a lot of pigs, a sounder they call them, rustling in the long grass where they could not see them. And they had ridden up to a little village and got some men to go into the grass making noises, and some of the natives had brought their dogs with them; and all the pigs had come out and they had ridden after the biggest. They got right away from the long grass at once and saw no more of it, except little patches that they scarcely noticed; in fact the one beside which we all met they never noticed at all, nor did the pig; or, if he did, he went straight for it because it reminded him of home; nor did the first horse, nor his rider. And they all went into the well.

'The pig climbed on to the horse's back, to keep himself out of the water; and the horse kept on rolling sideways as he swam, so as to put the pig back in the well. And that is another unusual thing to see, I mean a pig riding a horse; but, again, one should not disbelieve it merely on that account. I don't claim to have seen it myself, but the man who killed the pig saw it; in fact he killed it actually in the saddle. He killed the pig first because it seemed to make more room in the well, especially considering how near his tusks kept coming to the shoulder-blades of the man who was hanging by one arm from the bottom step. And then he pulled the man out. Getting the horse out was the hardest job of the lot.'

'Did you lend them a hand with the horse?' asked Terbut, rather unnecessarily.

'Well, no,' said Jorkens, 'I was perfectly ready to, but the fellow took offence at a quite natural remark that I made in all innocence. It was a simple and harmless remark, and very much to the point. But he took offence at it.'

'What did you say to him?' I asked.

'I merely said,' replied Jorkens, '"Nice for their drinking water."'

12

FISH ROYAL

by A. P. Herbert

THE greatest of all novels about fishing is undoubtedly
Herman Melville's classic tale of *Moby Dick*, published
well over 150 years ago, yet still in print and enjoyed by
each new generation of readers. In the days of which
Melville writes, men went fishing for whales in small boats
with hand-held harpoons, and the encounters between
these fishermen and the mightiest creatures in the sea were
often epics of courage and endurance. Today, of course, the
species is endangered and only a handful of nations ignore
the world's reprobation and still hunt and slaughter them.
When, indeed, whales are spotted they attract world-wide
interest – as in the winter of 1988 when three of them were
trapped in the Arctic ice and the super-powers, America
and Russia, joined forces in a remarkable display of co-
operation to set the two survivors free.

True fishermen everywhere admire the whale, and when the
creatures sometimes unfortunately beach themselves on our
coasts they are the first to lend a hand to try and get them back
to sea. Though such an event may not seem ideal material for a
humorous story, such is the case with 'Fish Royal' by A. P.
Herbert. Sir Alan Herbert, as he is sometimes better known,
was initially a barrister, later a politician, but first and foremost a comic writer who was one of the most popular contributors to *Punch* magazine for half a century. His stories of
the litigious Albert Haddock and his battles with the law are
deservedly regarded as classics of comedy. This particular

story does not feature Mr. Haddock, however, but is still a quite hilarious courtroom farce concerning the repercussions on a small fishing village of the discovery of a dead whale washed up on its beach.

FISH ROYAL

TINRIB, RUMBLE, AND OTHERS *v.* THE KING AND QUEEN

(Before Mr Justice Wool)

In this unusual action, the hearing of which was begun today, an interesting point is raised concerning the rights and duties of the Crown in connection with a dead whale.

Sir Ethelred Rutt, K.C., for the plaintiffs, said: May it please your lordship, this action is brought by Mr Tinrib, Mr Rumble, and the other plaintiffs on behalf of the inhabitants of Pudding Magna, situated, melud, in the county of Dorset—

The Court: Where is Dorset?

Sir Ethelred: Melud, I have a map here. Dorset, melud, if your lordship will glance at the bottom left-hand corner – Dorset, melud, is, melud, Dorset—

The Court: Quite – quite. Get on, please, Sir Ethelred.

Sir Ethelred: I am greatly obliged to your lordship. Pudding Magna, melud, is situated in the northeast corner of Pudding Bay, or the Devil's Entry. The inhabitants are mainly fisher folk of lowly origin and modest means, and, so far as can be ascertained, the place is not referred to in any of the works of Mr. Thomas Hardy, Mr. William Wordsworth, or any other writer—

The Court: O si sic omnes!

Sir Ethelred: Ha! Melud, in the night of the 21st June last a dead whale was washed up on the shore of Pudding Bay, at a point southwest by south from the township of Pudding Magna. Now, the whale, melud, together with the sturgeon and the swan, is Fish Royal, and belongs to the King; or, to be precise, the head of the whale belongs to His Majesty the King and the tail to Her Majesty the Queen. Your lordship will recall the case of *Rex* v. *Monday* (1841), 3 A.C., which decided the latter point.

The Court: I recall nothing of the kind.

Sir Ethelred: Your lordship is very good. The loyal inhabitants of Pudding Magna, melud, made haste to extract from the carcass of the whale the whalebone, the blubber, and other valuable and perishable portions, with the intention, I am instructed, of holding them in trust for the Crown. And I may say at once that any other construction of their motives will be most strenuously resisted, if necessary, by sworn evidence. Three days later, melud, the wind, which had been northerly, shifted to the prevailing quarter, which is southeast—

Sir Wilfred Knocknee, K.C.: You mean southwest.

Sir Ethelred: I am very greatly obliged to me learned friend. Me learned friend is perfectly right, melud; the prevailing wind is southwest, melud; and, melud, on the fifth day the presence of the whale began to be offensive to the inhabitants of Pudding Magna. They therefore looked with confidence to the Crown to remove to a more convenient place the remnant of the Crown's property—

Sir Wilfred (aside): For which they had no use.

Sir Ethelred: Really, melud, me learned friend must not whisper insinuations of that kind under his breath; really, melud, I am entitled to resent, melud—

The Court: Go on, Sir Ethelred.

Sir Ethelred: Your lordship is extraordinarily handsome and good. Accordingly, melud, the Mayor of Pudding Magna, addressed a humble petition to the Home Secretary, melud, begging him to acquaint His Majesty with the arrival of his property and praying for its instant removal. And by a happy afterthought, melud, a copy of this petition was sent to the Minister of Agriculture and Fisheries.

Happy, melud, for this reason, that the original communication appears to have escaped the notice of the Home Secretary entirely. At the Ministry of Agriculture and Fisheries, however, the Mayor's letter was handed to a public servant named Sleep, a newcomer to the Service, and one, it seems, who combined with a fertile imagination an unusual incapacity for the conduct of practical affairs. This gentleman has now left the public service, melud, and will be called.

It appears, melud, that, when the Mayor's letter had been lying unconsidered on Mr Sleep's desk for several days, the following telegram was handed to him:

To the King London whale referred to in previous communication now in advanced stages decomposition humbly petition prompt action.
                                                    Tinrib

Mr Sleep, melud, according to his own account, turning the matter over in his sagacious mind, at once hit upon a solution which would be likely to satisfy the requirements of His Majesty's Treasury with regard to public economy. Two days later, therefore, a letter was addressed to the Director of the Natural History Museum informing him that an unusually fine specimen of *Balœna Biscayensis* was now lying in Pudding Bay and that the Minister was authorized by His Majesty to offer the whale to the Museum in trust for the nation, the Museum to bear the charges of collection and transport.

On July 3rd, melud, the Secretary to the Natural History Museum replied that he was asked by the Director to express his regret that, owing to lack of space, the Museum was unable to accept His Majesty's gracious offer. He was to add that the Museum was already in possession of three fine specimens of *Balœna Biscayensis*.

Melud, for some days, it appears, Mr Sleep took no further action. Meanwhile, melud, the whale had passed from the advanced to the penultimate stage of decomposition, and had begun to poison the sea at high water, thereby gravely impairing the fishermen's livelihood. Mr Tinrib, melud, was in constant, if one-sided, correspondence with Mr Sleep; and on the 12th of July, melud, Mr Sleep lunched with a friend and colleague at the Admiralty, Mr Sloe. While they were engaged, melud, upon the discussion of fish, the topic of whales naturally arose, and Mr Sleep, melud, unofficially, melud, expressed to Mr Sloe the opinion that the Ministry of Agriculture and Fisheries would be willing to grant to the Admiralty the use of the whale for the purposes of target practice; and he suggested that one of His Majesty's ships should be immediately detailed to tow His Majesty's whale out to sea. He also pointed out the peculiar advantages of such a target for the exercise of such vessels as were called upon to fire at submarines. Mr Sloe, melud, undertook to explore the opinion of the Admiralty on the proposal, and the conference broke up.

That was on the 12th. On the 17th, melud, Mr Sloe unofficially, melud, at a further lunch, intimated to Mr Sleep that he could find no support among their Lordships of the Admiralty for the proposal of the Ministry of Agriculture and Fisheries; for, while excellent practice was to be had from a disappearing target, their Lordships could not sanction the expenditure of ammunition on a target which must, at most ranges, be quite invisible. Further, it was their opinion that by the date of the autumn firing practices the whale would have suffered dissolution by the ordinary processes of nature.

The inhabitants of Pudding Magna, melud, did not share this view. On the 20th, melud, Mr Tinrib and a deputation waited upon Mr Sleep. They pointed out to Mr Sleep that all fishing was suspended in Pudding Bay; that Pudding Magna was now barely inhabitable except on the rare occasions of a northerly wind; that the majority of the citizens had fled to the hills and were living in huts and caves. They further inquired, melud, whether it would be lawful for the fishermen themselves to destroy the whale, so far as that could be done, with explosives, and, if so, whether the Crown would refund the cost of the explosives, which might be considerable. As to this, melud, Mr Sleep was unable to accept the responsibility of expressing an opinion; but the whale was undoubtedly Crown property, and he questioned gravely whether the Treasury would sanction the expenditure of public money on the destruction of Crown property by private citizens. He also pointed out that the Treasury if approached would be likely to require a strict account of any whalebone, blubber, and other material extracted from the whale's carcass. Mention of explosives, however, had suggested to his mind that possibly the War Office might be interested in the whale, and he undertook to inquire. The deputation agreed, melud, that this perhaps would be the better course, and withdrew.

On the 24th, melud, a letter was dispatched to the War Office pointing out that the whale now lying in Pudding Bay offered excellent opportunities for the training of engineers in the removal of obstacles, and could well be made the centre of any amphibious operations, landing-parties, invasions, etc., which might form part of the forthcoming manoeuvres. The

War Office would doubtless take note of the convenient proximity of the whale to the Tank Corps Depot at Lulworth.

On the 31st, melud, the War Office replied that the destruction of whales by tanks was no longer considered a practicable operation of war, and that no part of the forthcoming manoeuvres would be amphibious.

From this date, melud, Mr Sleep seems to have abandoned his efforts. At any rate, on the 4th of August, Mr Tinrib received the following evasive and disgraceful communication:

WHALE, CARCASE OF

Dear Sir,

I am desired by the Minister of Agriculture and Fisheries to observe that your representations to this Department appear to have been made under a misapprehension. It should hardly be necessary to state that the whale is not a fish but a mammal. I am therefore to express regret that the Ministry of Agriculture and Fisheries can accept no responsibility in the matter.

In these circumstances, melud, the inhabitants, or I should say the *late* inhabitants, of Pudding Magna have been compelled to institute these proceedings, and humbly pray—
The case was adjourned.

13

FISHING IN BADEN PERFECT

by Ernest Hemingway

THE great fishing novel of the twentieth century is Ernest Hemingway's *The Old Man and the Sea* (1952) and its stark description of the battle between the fisherman and his catch somehow encapsulates the very essence of the attraction of angling. It has certainly fired the imagination of uncounted readers to try the sport – and just as certainly brought back memories for any veteran fisherman who has read it.

Because Hemingway is so firmly associated with stories of physical courage told in terse dialogue, it will probably surprise most readers to find his name in this collection. No one will need reminding that fishing was one of his passions, of course, but to find him writing about the sport with irony and amusement will probably come as something of a shock to the reader as it was to me when I discovered the following item. It was a chance remark by one of Hemingway's biographers, C.A. Fenton, that the author had a strong sense of humour and that 'comic elements can be found in some of his earlier writings' that promoted my research and led to the discovery of 'Fishing In Baden Perfect' which he wrote in September 1922. In fact, it proved to be one of several stories Hemingway has written about his fishing exploits in America, Canada and Europe during the early days of his literary career, all of which display his mastery of descriptive writing. What this particular story also shows is that Hemingway was equally adept at the comic turn of phrase as well as the humorous observation of people . . .

FISHING IN BADEN PERFECT

If you want to go fishing in the Black Forest, you want to get up about four hours before the first Schwarzwald rooster begins to shift from one leg to the other and decide that it's time to crow. You need at least that much time to get through the various legal labyrinths in order to get on to the stream before dark.

In the first place the Black Forest is not the sweep of black forest that its name suggests. It is a chain of mountains cut up by railroads, valleys full of rank potato crops, pasture land, brown chalets and gravel-bottomed trout streams, broken out all over with enormous hotels run by Germanised Swiss who have mastered the art of making four beefsteaks grow where only one was cut by the butcher and where you waken up in the morning to find that the falling mark has cut your hotel bill to $3.75 a week and that the price of James E. Pepper Kentucky rye whiskey is 90 cents a bottle.

A Swiss hotelkeeper can raise prices with the easy grace of a Pullman car poker shark backing a pat full house, but the mark can fall faster than even a Swiss in good training can hoist the cost of living. A properly run race between a well-conditioned Swiss hotelkeeper and a fast-falling mark would provide an international financial spectacle that would bring the financial fans to their feet as one man, but my last kronen would go on the mark. In spite of it being the monetary medium that is in daily use in the Einsteinian household, the mark still seems affected by the laws of gravitation.

All of which and none of which has anything to do with the trout fishing in the Black Forest. Triberg consists of a single steep street lined by steep hotels. It is in a steep valley and a cool breeze is said to blow down the valley in wintertime. No one has ever been in Triberg in the wintertime to verify this legend but eight hundred sweltering tourists would gladly lay their right hands over where their hearts ought to be, if their hearts are in the right place, and swear there never has been a breeze of any kind in the summertime.

We landed in Triberg after a five-hour train ride from Freiberg. We had originally planned to walk across the Black Forest but we gave this up when we saw the crowd of German tourists touring in and out of all the roads leading to the woods. Our first disappointment was in finding that the Black Forest was no forest but just a lot of wooded hills and highly cultivated valleys, and our second was in discovering that you couldn't go fifteen yards along any of the wilder and more secluded roads without running into between six and eight Germans, their heads shaved, their knees bare, cock feathers in their hats, sauerkraut on their breath, the wanderlust in their eyes and a collection of aluminium cooking utensils clashing against their legs as they walked.

As I may have said, we landed in Triberg. It was the end of a five-hour ride with two changes and four hours of standing in the aisle while large and unhappy Germans and their large and marcelled wives pushed by us again and again with profuse apologies, and I don't know what aims.

'The proprietor will fix it up for you,' said the head porter of the hotel. 'He has a friend who has a fishing.'

We went into the bar where the friend who had the fishing and six of his friends were sitting at a table and playing a game that looked like pinochle. The proprietor talked with the friend, who has one of the porcupine-quill haircuts that are all the rage this year, and the friend pounded the table with his fist while the rest of the table roared and laughed.

The proprietor came over to our table.

'They all make jokes,' he said. 'He says if you pay him two dollars you can fish all you want for the rest of your life.'

Now we are all very familiar with the German when he starts making jokes about the dollar, and suggests that he be paid for such-and-such in dollars. It is a foul and nefarious habit. If it were allowed to go unchecked, it would soon force all Canadians and Americans back to Sarnia, Ontario, or Kokomo, Indiana. It is a habit that needs to be sat on with all severity.

There was a lot of dickering. The friend and his friends ceased laughing. We grew stern and strong and silent. The porter grew placatory. The atmosphere grew tense. We finally compromised by agreeing to pay 1,200 marks for the fishing unseen. We went to bed happy. We were the owner of a fishing in the Black Forest. We turned over in our thirty-seven-cents-a-night bed in the regal suite of the largest hotel in Triberg and kicked the eiderdown quilt onto the floor. After all, there seemed to be some justice in the world.

In the morning we got our tackle together and went down to breakfast. The porter, who is another Swiss passing as German, came up.

'I have news for you. It is not so easy. You must first obtain the permit of the police. You must get a *fischkarte*.'

[152]

I pass over the next two days. They were spent in the offices of the Kingdom of Baden, now doing business as a republic of sorts, and consisted of conversations like the following:

We enter an office where a number of clerks are sitting around while stern-looking soldiers scratch the small of their backs with the pommels of their swords, or is it only saddles that have pommels?

We, Mr [William] Bird and myself, speak. '*Vere ist der Burgomeister?*'

The clerks eye us and go on writing. The soldiers look out of the window at the large stone monument to the war of 1870. Finally a clerk looks up and points to an inner door. There are a line of people outside. We are at the end of the line and finally get in.

Us, Mr Bird, who is the European manager of the Consolidated Press, and myself speak: '*Bitte, Herr Burgomeister. We wollen der fischkarten. We wollen to gefischen goen.*'

The Burgomeister looks at us and says, '*Nix. Nein.*' That is the only understandable point of his discourse.

'*Das fischenkarten,*' we explain sweetly.

'*Nix,*' he says. '*Nein,*' and points to the door.

We go out. This continues indefinitely.

When we finally, by tracing the person who owned it down at his factory where he makes lightning rods or hairbrushes, found where the fishing was located we were informed by another fine-looking burgomeister that we would have to give up our attempts at getting a fishing licence in Triberg altogether and go to Nussbach. We didn't know where Nussbach was. It looked hopeless. We resolved to fish instead.

The stream was a beauty. The friend who owned it was evidently so busy making hair tonic or shoe buttons in his factory that he never fished himself and the trout bit as fast as you could wet a line. We took all we wanted and repeated the next day. On the third day my conscience bothered me.

'We ought to go to Nussbach and get that permit to fish,' I suggested.

[153]

We went to Nussbach with the aid of a map. No one seemed to know where the burgomeister's office was. Finally we found him in a little shed across the street from the churchyard where a group of schoolboys were being given squad drill. We had been informed as to the dire penalties that were waiting for those who fished without a Badischer permit. Poaching was rigorously punished.

Mr Bird, who answers to the name of Bill, can talk German. But he doesn't think he can. I, on the contrary, cannot talk German at all, but I think I can. Therefore, I usually dominate the conversation. Mr Bird says that my system of talking German is to pronounce English with an Italian accent.

'*Ve wishen der fischenkarten,*' I said, bowing low.

The Burgomeister looked at me over his steel-rimmed spectacles.

'*Ja?*' he said.

'*Ve wishen der fischenkarten comme ça,*' I said very firmly, showing him the yellow card the friend had loaned us to locate the water.

'*Ja,*' he said, examining the card. '*Das ist gut wasser.*'

'*Can ve gefischen in it?*' I asked.

'*Ja, ja,*' answered the Burgomeister.

'Come on, Bill,' I said, 'let's go.'

We have been fishing the water ever since. No one has stopped us. Some day, doubtless, we will be arrested. I shall appeal to the Burgomeister of Nussbach. He is a splendid man. But I remember distinctly his having told us we could fish all the good water.

14

THE LITTLE FISHES

by H. E. Bates

THERE are few better writers of short stories than H. E. Bates and few more memorable characters from the English countryside than his Uncle Silas. Bates, of course, has written about the countryside and its people with unique insight, and it is not surprising to discover that the irascible Uncle Silas – poacher, drinker, rustic gourmet, ladies' man and fisherman, par excellence – was based on one of his relatives, a certain Joseph Betts who lived all his life in a tiny, rural Bedfordshire village. 'Silas,' Bates wrote in 1957, 'is an authentic figure. The scenes and incidents in which he appears are, too, very close to life. They are all things which have the dearest associations for me in memory.'

H. E. Bates was a keen angler, and there are mentions of the sport to be found in several of his novels as well as in a famous short story, 'Fishing' about two old eel fishermen which appears in the collection, *Day's End* (1928). But he is undoubtedly at the very top of his form when writing about Uncle Silas, using himself as the small and wondering observer of the old man's fund of knowledge. So there is, therefore, no question about plumping for a tale in which he appears, 'The Little Fishes' – for in it we are introduced to the art of fishing, Uncle Silas style, in a manner which is both highly evocative and wryly amusing. It is also one of those rare stories that remains in the memory long after it is finished.

THE LITTLE FISHES

My Uncle Silas was very fond of fishing. It was an occupation that helped to keep him from thinking too much about work and also about how terribly hard it was.

If you went through the bottom of my Uncle Silas's garden, past the gooseberry bushes, the rhubarb and the pigsties, you came to a path that went alongside a wood where primroses grew so richly in spring that they blotted out the floor of oak and hazel leaves. In summer wild strawberries followed the primroses and by July the meadows beyond the wood were frothy with meadow-sweet, red clover and the seed of tall soft grasses.

At the end of the second meadow a little river, narrow in parts and bellying out into black deep pools in others, ran along between willows and alders, occasional clumps of dark high reeds and a few wild crab trees. Some of the pools, in July, would be white with water lilies, and snakes would swim across the light flat leaves in the sun. Moorhens talked to each other behind the reeds and water rats would plop suddenly out of sight under clumps of yellow monkey flower.

Here in this little river, my Uncle Silas used to tell me when I was a boy, 'the damn pike used to be as big as hip-popottomassiz.'

'Course they ain't so big now,' he would say. 'Nor yit the tench. Nor yit the perch. Nor yit the—'

'Why aren't they so big?'

'Well, I'm a-talkin' about fifty years agoo. Sixty years agoo. Very near seventy years agoo.'

'If they were so big then,' I said, 'all that time ago, they ought to be even bigger now.'

'Not the ones we catched,' he said. 'They ain't there.'

You couldn't, as you see from this, fox my Uncle Silas very easily, but I was at all times a very inquisitive, persistent little boy.

'How big were the tench?' I said.

'Well, I shall allus recollect one as me and Sammy Twizzle caught,' he said. 'Had to lay it in a pig trough to carry it home.'

'And how big were the perch?'

'Well,' he said, rolling his eye in recollection, in that way he had of bringing the wrinkled lid slowly down over it, very like a fish ancient in craftiness himself, 'I don' know as I can jistly recollect the size o' that one me and Arth Sugars nipped out of a September morning one time. But I do know as I cleaned up the back fin and used it for horse comb for about twenty year.'

'Oh! Uncle Silas,' I would say, 'let's go fishing! Let's go and see if they're still as big as hippopotomassiz!'

But it was not always easy, once my Uncle Silas had settled under the trees at the end of the garden on a hot July afternoon, to persuade him to see if the fish were as big as they used to be. Nevertheless I was, as I say, a very inquisitive, persistent little boy and finally my Uncle Silas would roll over, take the red handkerchief off his face and grunt:

'If you ain't the biggest whittle-breeches I ever knowed I'll goo t'Hanover. Goo an' git the rod and bring a bit o' dough. They'll be no peace until you do, will they?'

'Shall I bring the rod for you too?'

'*Rod?*' he said. 'For me. *Rod?*' He let fall over his eye a tremulous bleary fish-like lid of scorn. 'When me and Sammy Twizzle went a-fishin, all we had to catch 'em with wur we bare hands and a drop o' neck-oil.'

'What's neck-oil?'

'Never you mind,' he said. 'You git the rod and I'll git the neck-oil.'

And presently we would be walking out of the garden, past the wood and across the meadows, I carrying the rod, the dough and perhaps a piece of caraway cake in a paper bag, my Uncle Silas waddling along in his stony-coloured corduroy trousers, carrying the neck-oil.

Sometimes I would be very inquisitive about the neck-oil, which was often pale greenish-yellow, rather the colour of cowslip, or perhaps of parsnips, and sometimes purplish-red, rather the colour of elderberries, or perhaps of blackberries or plums.

On one occasion I noticed that the neck-oil was very light in colour, almost white, or perhaps more accurately like straw-coloured water.

'Is it a new sort of neck-oil you've got?' I said.

'New flavour.'

'What is it made of?'

'Taters.'

'And you've got two bottles today,' I said.

'Must try to git used to the new flavour.'

'And do you think,' I said, 'we shall catch a bigger fish now that you've got a new kind of neck-oil?'

'Shouldn't be a bit surprised, boy,' he said, 'if we don't git one as big as a donkey.'

That afternoon it was very hot and still as we sat under the shade of a big willow, by the side of a pool that seemed to have across it an oiled black skin broken only by minutest winks of sunlight when the leaves of the willow parted softly in gentle turns of air.

'This is the place where me and Sammy tickled that big 'un out,' my Uncle Silas said.

'The one you carried home in a pig trough?'

'That's the one.'

I said how much I too should like to catch one I could take home in a pig trough and my Uncle Silas said:

'Well, you never will if you keep whittlin' and talkin' and ompolodgin' about.' My Uncle Silas was the only man in the world who ever used the word ompolodgin'. It was a very expressive word and when my Uncle Silas accused you of ompolodgin' it was a very serious matter. It meant that you had buttons on your bottom and if you didn't drop it he would damn well ding your ear. 'You gotta sit still and wait and not keep fidgetin' and very like in another half-hour you'll see a big'un layin' aside o' that log. But not if you keep ompolodgin'! See?'

'Yes, Uncle.'

'That's why I bring the neck-oil,' he said. 'It quiets you down so's you ain't a-whittlin' and a-ompolodgin' all the time.'

'Can I have a drop of neck-oil?'

'When you git thirsty,' my Uncle Silas said, 'there's that there spring in the next medder.'

After this my Uncle Silas took a good steady drink of neck-oil and settled down with his back against the tree. I put a big lump of paste on my hook and dropped it into the pool. The only fish I could see in the pool were shoals of little silver tiddlers that flickered about a huge fallen willow log a yard or two upstream or came to play inquisitively about my little white and scarlet float, making it quiver up and down like the trembling scraps of sunlight across the water.

Sometimes the bread paste got too wet and slipped from the hook and I quietly lifted the rod from the water and put another lump on the hook. I tried almost not to breathe as I did all this and every time I took the rod out of the water I glanced furtively at my Uncle Silas to see if he thought I was ompolodgin'.

Every time I looked at him I could see that he evidently didn't think so. He was always far too busy with the neck-oil.

I suppose we must have sat there for nearly two hours on that hot windless afternoon of July, I not speaking a word and trying not to breathe as I threw my little float across the water, my Uncle Silas never uttering a sound either except for a drowsy grunt or two as he uncorked one bottle of neck-oil or felt to see if the other was safe in his jacket pocket.

All that time there was no sign of a fish as big as a hippo-potamus or even of one you could take home in a pig trough and all the time my Uncle Silas kept tasting the flavour of the neck-oil, until at last his head began to fall forward on his chest. Soon all my bread paste was gone and I got so afraid of disturbing my Uncle Silas that I scotched my rod to the fallen log and walked into the next meadow to get myself a drink of water from the spring.

The water was icy cold from the spring and very sweet and good and I wished I had brought myself a bottle too, so that I could fill it and sit back against a tree, as my Uncle Silas did, and pretend that it was neck-oil.

Ten minutes later, when I got back to the pool, my Uncle Silas was fast asleep by the tree trunk, one bottle empty by his side and the other still in his jacket pocket. There was, I thought, a remarkable expression on his face, a wonderful rosy fogginess about his mouth and nose and eyes.

But what I saw in the pool, as I went to pick my rod from the water, was a still more wonderful thing.

During the afternoon the sun had moved some way round and under the branches of the willow, so that now, at the first touch of evening, there were clear bands of pure yellow light across the pool.

In one of these bands of light, by the fallen log, lay a long lean fish, motionless as a bar of steel, just under the water, basking in the evening sun.

When I woke my Uncle Silas he came to himself with a fumbling start, red eyes only half open, and I thought for a moment that perhaps he would ding my ear for ompolodgin'.

'But it's as big as a hippopotamus,' I said. 'It's as big as the one in the pig trough.'

'Wheer, boy? Wheer?'

When I pointed out the fish, my Uncle Silas could not, at first, see it lying there by the log. But after another nip of neck-oil he started to focus it correctly.

'By Jingo, that's a big 'un,' he said. 'By Jingo, that's a walloper.'

'What sort is it?'

'Pike,' he said. 'Git me a big lump o' paste and I'll dangle it a-top of his nose.'

'The paste has all gone.'

'Then give us a bit o' caraway and we'll tiddle him up wi' that.'

'I've eaten all the caraway,' I said. 'Besides, you said you and Sammy Twizzle used to catch them with your hands. You said you used to tickle their bellies—'

'Well, that wur—'

'Get him! Get him! Get him!' I said. 'He's as big as a donkey!'

Slowly, and with what I thought was some reluctance, my Uncle Silas heaved himself to his feet. He lifted the bottle from his pocket and took a sip of neck-oil. Then he slapped the cork back with the palm of his hand, wiped his lips with the back of his hand and put the bottle back in his pocket.

'Now you stan' back,' he said, 'and dammit, don't git ompolodgin'!'

I stood back. My Uncle Silas started to creep along the fallen willow log on his hands and knees. Below him, in the band of sunlight, I could see the long dark lean pike, basking.

For nearly two minutes my Uncle Silas hovered on the end of the log. Then slowly he balanced himself on one hand and dipped his other into the water. Over the pool it was marvellously, breathlessly still and I knew suddenly that this was how it had been in the good great old days, when my Uncle Silas and Sammy Twizzle had caught the mythical mammoth ones, fifty years before.

'God A'mighty!' my Uncle Silas suddenly yelled. 'I'm a-gooin' over!'

My Uncle Silas was indeed gooin' over. Slowly, like a turning spit, the log started heeling, leaving my Uncle Silas half-slipping, half-dancing at its edge, like a man on a greasy pole.

In terror I shut my eyes. When I opened them and looked again my Uncle Silas was just coming up for air, yelling 'God A'mighty, boy, I believe you ompolodged!'

I thought for a moment he was going to be very angry with me. Instead he started to cackle with crafty, devilish, stentorian laughter, his wet lips dribbling, his eyes more fiery than ever under the dripping water, his right hand triumphant as he snatched it up from the stream.

'Jist managed to catch it, boy,' he yelled, and in triumph he held up the bottle of neck-oil.

And somewhere downstream, startled by his shout, a whole host of little tiddlers jumped from the water, dancing in the evening sun.

15

THE ONE THAT NEARLY GOT AWAY

by Maurice Richardson

For thirty years and more until his death in 1978, Maurice Richardson was regarded as one of the most imaginative and wide-ranging literary journalists in Britain – as well as a larger-than-life character who had few equals in the city of London. Built like a boxer (he had actually been a fine amateur fighter in his youth), he attacked life with gusto and had a large circle of friends, many of whom – like the self-styled 'Great Beast', Aleister Crowley, and the 'Yorkshire Yogi', Dr. Alexander Cannon – were as eccentric as himself. Though perhaps more devoted to wining and dining than physical activity in his later years, he retained a strong interest in sport with boxing, wrestling, shooting and angling being his favourites.

Maurice Richardson contributed to numerous magazines like *Punch* and *The New Statesman* as well as to newspapers such as *The Times*, *The Observer* and *The Daily Telegraph*, and it is in their pages that his observations on sport are mainly to be found. He does, though, mention fishing in two of his novels, *Strong Man Needed* (1931) which features Lord Cadwallow who fishes in the Regent's Park Canal where it passes his London home, and *The Bad Companions* (1936) about two rogues with a hilarious line in tall stories. However, Richardson's tallest stories of all are to be found in his book, *The Exploits of Engelbrecht* (1950) which is subtitled, 'Abstracted From The Chronicles of The Surrealist Sportsman's Club'. Engelbrecht is a dwarf surrealist boxer who shares his creator's interest in sport and in the story which follows takes part in a fishing competition – but a contest, be advised, that could only have been devised in the uniquely imaginative mind of Maurice Richardson ...

THE ONE THAT NEARLY GOT AWAY

Of all the events in the surrealist sporting calendar few attract such a passionately excited following as the Annual Angling Championship, held in the canal round behind the gasworks, just where the town drain comes in.

Unlike the ordinary humdrum disciple of Izaak Walton, your Surrealist Piscator can always be certain of catching something – generally something damned dangerous, if you ask me – and many's the deathly struggle I've witnessed on the bank as terrified anglers tried to put back things that would have been far better never hooked. It was, therefore, with the keenest anticipation, and no little misgiving, that I accepted the invitation of my friend Engelbrecht, the dwarf surrealist boxer, an all-round sportsman if ever there was one, to make up a party to watch him compete for the trophy.

A room had been booked for me at the Fisherman's Eternal Rest, and when I arrived I found the little bar-parlour thronged with old friends and fiends, all keen amateurs of the gentle art, fortifying their nerves with rounds of double mandragora laced with poppy against the morrow's encounters with the perils of the deep. Meanwhile, in the Hashish Room at the end of the passage, Dr Sadismus, the surrealist surgeon, then at the height of his fame owing to his daring operation for the removal of a human finger from the bowels of a sewing machine, was organising, with the assistance of a posse of psychiatrists, a first aid post.

The talk was all of the catch that might be expected. In accordance with his usual general custom, the Id, that munificent patron of surrealist sport, had contributed lavishly to stocking the canal, and some really sensational captures were anticipated. Rumour had it that the prize was a 600-year-old giant pike from the Fens, the same who in 1448 snatched the Bishop of Ely from his mule as he rode the towpath.

'You stand a fine chance of hooking him, my wee man,' chaffed Chippy de Zoete, patting Engelbrecht on the head. 'Dwarfs are his favourite bait.'

Just then Lizard Bayliss, my friend's devoted but highly strung manager, who had been for a stroll along the canal bank, tottered in and collapsed in a trembling heap. 'There's things in that there water that never ought to have been thought of,' he told us.

After a restless night disturbed more than once by screams, I hurried down to find the rest of our party with grave faces. News had just been brought that the lock-keeper and his entire family had been dragged under.

The beat Engelbrecht had drawn for the early morning rise was a stretch of jet black water between the jubilee gasometer and the municipal slaughter house. A dank mist lay over the canal. The vampire bats were out in swarms. The bot-fly waltzed in virid clouds. You could hardly have had a better surrealist fishing day. From their stand on top of the gasometer the Band of the Asylum Workers Union struck up the *March of the Wooden Zombies*. Presently the quavering tones of Dreamy Dan, the surrealist umpire, announced the start of play.

'Crikey,' said Lizard Bayliss, 'do you see what I see?'

Floating on the surface of the water was a fleet of five pound notes. Lizard was in the act of bending down to pick one up when a voice behind him said: 'I shouldn't touch that if I were you. It's surface bait laid on from below to catch the unwary fisherman.'

It was our old friend the Oldest Member who had tottered out of his tomb swathed in a shroud of Donegal tweed to see how we were faring. Under his supervision we assembled Engelbrecht's tackle, a somewhat eclectic assortment that included a rod as big as a crane and a float with a great chapel bell attached. Then Lizard Bayliss backed the Black Maria containing the bait down to the water's edge.

There was some heated discussion over the choice of bait. Engelbrecht wanted to fish a Barnet By-Pass, a beautifully made facsimile of a suburban housewife with a lot of brightly coloured feathers in her hat, just the kind of gaudy affair calculated to catch the eye of the tiro. But the O.M. counselled a more sober-looking lure known as a College Chaplain, one of Clarkson's most skilful pieces of human dry fly tying, in cork and composition with bespoke tailoring and a neat little hump to conceal the hook. 'Did you ever see anything so lifelike?' he said.

'Too damned lifelike altogether,' said Lizard. 'Lumme, did you see that? I believe he winked at me.'

'I hope he did no such thing,' said the O.M. severely. 'Fishing with human bait is barred. We had to disqualify de Lautréamont for that in '53.'

Our preparations were now complete. Engelbrecht took a

firm grip on the rod and brought all his dwarf strength to bear. The first cast pulled down the façade of a stationer's shop in Fore Street. The second hooked a tray of glass eyes. The third was a fizzer. Fathom after fathom of line shot out and away out of sight into the mist. But when we took roll call afterwards Lizard Bayliss was missing.

Presently there was an earsplitting peal from the chapel bell far out across the black water. Engelbrecht began reeling in. Soon we caught sight of a vast domed shape looming through the mist. It was the float with Lizard Bayliss sitting on top of it. We gaffed him ashore. It was obvious he would never be fit to fish again so we packed him off to the psychiatrist's.

By now the canal bank was a scene of frightful carnage but precious little piscage. Nodder Fothergill, on our right, had landed something I never expected to see outside the canvases of Hieronymus Bosch and was fighting a losing battle trying to put it back. Bones Barlow had plunged in after a Nereid and had his waders rotted off by acid. Little Charlie Wapentake had fouled the Grendal family *mère et fils*. So critical, indeed, did the situation become that just before lunch the order was given to repulse boarders. We all dropped our rods and rushed to the rescue of whoever needed help most.

The score at lunch time was depressing. Several of our best anglers had either been dragged under, pulled out to sea, or else were raving in the schizophrenic ward. Father Carfax, the Id's chaplain, had been lost with all hands during a plucky exorcism ceremony. Some interesting inanimate objects had been caught, including a calculating machine which, as the O.M. observed, would come in handy for telling fishing stories. Salvador Dali had landed a chest of drawers of fifty-seven pounds weight, the contents of which had to be sent to the local police. But no one had had a bite from the man-eating pike and there was a rumour that Chippy de Zoete had been seen slipping some sticks of dynamite into his waistcoat pocket.

[168]

After lunch we drew the Fever Hospital Bend, a ticklish stretch where you have to fish off a narrow asphalt track with a fifty-foot drop into the rubbish dump at your back. I attached a lure known as The Hanged Man and we cast far out into the murk, now thickened by fumes from the chemical works. 'They can never resist this one,' said Engelbrecht with typical angler's optimism. But they could. When the bell tolled and we reeled in we found nothing save a shipwrecked pleasure party clinging to the float. The bait was untouched except for a notice which some underwater character had tied round its neck. It read: *'Insufficiently Verisimilitudinous. Better Luck Next Time.'*

We showed it to the Oldest Member who was engrossed in Chetham's *Vade Mecum*. 'That's the Fisher King,' he said. 'A mythological figure who haunts these waters. Reputed to be a cousin of the Id's. Got a very keen sense of humour. He collected one of those new pens that write under water from one of our members last year.'

A rattle of musketry on our left denoted that yet another landing party had been repulsed. But still not a bite.

The Oldest Member looked up from Sir Humphry Davey's *Salmonia* which he had been perusing. 'I'm afraid you're having very poor sport,' he said. 'The catch of the day so far is a seven league boot.'

Engelbrecht was down at the reel end of the rod. He rang through on the 'phone to ask me to come and take a turn, while he had a chat with the O.M. When he came back his face was set and grim. He was wearing a frogman's suit of black india rubber and a clerical collar. 'Hook me, pal,' he said, 'hook me in the hump.'

'But dwarfie,' I said, 'you're not going in yourself?'

'It's the only way,' he said.

'But you're human, aren't you? You'll be disqualified.'

'The O.M. says not. He says it's all right if you bait your own hook. You'll hold the rod for me, pal?'

'Well,' I said. 'I hope you know what you're doing.'

'I hope I do too,' he said.

'Greater love hath no angler than this,' said the voice of the O.M. behind us.

I fixed the hook tight into the artificial hump and paid out enough line to reach all the way. I gave the hook a final tug to make sure it was good and firm. Then I cast. The dwarf-baited hook flew out through the thick night air far over the water. It fell with a light splash. I reeled in a few hundred fathoms to keep him riding on top of the water and gave the line a couple of jerks to make it seem as if he was drowning. Then I lit my pipe.

Presently I heard Engelbrecht's voice on the intercom. 'They're coming for me, pal,' he said. 'I can see their eyes all round me. It's just a question which one gets me first. Soon as you hear me holler you got to strike for all you're worth.'

Next moment the bell pealed out the Angelus and Engelbrecht's voice yelled in my ear: 'Strike like beggary.' I turned on the donkey engine full steam ahead and struck.

The line ran out at a rate of knots. There was silence for some time. Then Engelbrecht came through again. 'You there, pal? He's hooked good. It's the giant pike all right.'

'How do you know?'

'He's swallowed me and I just picked up a bishop's mitre with the name Ely on the sweat band. Play him, pal. Play him for all you're worth. You got to land him before the season ends.'

In the months that followed I played that pike all over the network of our inland waterways, in and out of drains and culverts and subterranean streams known only to spæleologists. Sometimes when the line was right out I had to take the train to keep up with him. And always the Oldest Member was at my elbow ready to give sage counsel. 'Whatever happens we must head him off from the Fens,' he kept telling me. 'Black Fen, which is his home water, is known to be bottomless.'

It was the last week of the season and Engelbrecht had just 'phoned through, very faint, to say that his rations had run out. We were streaking along the Manchester Ship Canal with mighty few fathoms in hand. 'I'm afraid we've lost him,' said the Oldest Member. 'You'll have to order your little pal to abandon fish.' With a sob in my voice I told Engelbrecht to unhook himself. Suddenly we rounded a bend and caught sight of a bunch of theological students out for a walk with the bishop at their head. The pike must have seen them too. He leapt in a great green-yellow arc for the bank. But he was too weak, and before his jaws could close, the bishop, an old sportsman if ever there was one, had gaffed him in the gills with his umbrella. The ordination candidates formed a chain, clasping each other by the waist.

After a tremendous struggle we got him ashore and wired for Doctor Sadismus, who removed Engelbrecht, little the worse for wear. There was a good deal of controversy in surrealist piscatorial circles, but it was finally decided that the catch should stand. And you can see the pike stuffed, with the Bishop of Ely's mitre underneath, in the Fisherman's Eternal Rest.

16

TROUTMANSHIP

by Stephen Potter

THE art of better angling is a pursuit that has produced a veritable library of books written by expert fishermen from all over the world – plus a number of very amusing parodies of such instruction manuals by humorists like Alan d'Egville (*Calling All Coarse-Fishers*, 1949), Cliff Parker (*The Fishing Handbook to End All Fishing Handbooks*, 1974) and most notably of all, Stephen Potter, creator of the famous books of One-Upmanship. These volumes, which are now a part of the language, describe the gentle art of ensuring success in any chosen pursuit by demoralisation of your opponent.

Potter, who was a BBC radio producer and co-authored a highly popular series, 'How', with the comedienne, Joyce Grenfell, was very much the reluctant fisherman, and admitted it was his significant lack of success with rod and line that prompted him to write the following essay, 'Troutmanship' as one of the courses for his mythical 'Life-manship Correspondence College of One-Upmanship and Gameslifemastery.' The story also draws some of its inspiration from the style of the very first classic manual on angling by Izaak Walton – though the humour and ingenuity is unmistakably Potter's own. If the reader is not a better fisherman after perusing the next few pages – then he will at least be in a more amused frame of mind!

TROUTMANSHIP

What a complex world is here! Yet in the relatively small province of our little correspondence college we have made enormous headway and gained the thanks of all the fishership community by defining once and for all the two basic trout approaches, in one of which students are expected to satisfy the examiners.

Our decontamination reader in Trout, J. Hargreaves, is a pleasant teacher who plays the two-approach system admirably himself. With newcomers, he demonstrates this twoness with a pair of ordinary fishing rods, one of which is new, the other old.

Rodmanship

This basic gambit is, basically, the art of being one-up with one's rod. Most commonly, the man who still keeps his old rod is pitted against the man who has just bought a new one. Old Rod makes first move:

OLD ROD *(looking at New Rod's new rod)*: I like it. I like it. I like it. I like it. Of course I'm in my forties. I suppose my old one will see me through. Ought to. Ought to. Ought to.

NEW ROD *(countering implied criticism)*: I was sorry to see my last rod go. . . . But if one really *fishes* in water like this . . . you know . . . I suppose one kills about a rod a season? Mind you, if you don't go in for these acrobatic casts I'm always attempting rather unsuccessfully . . .

OLD ROD *(pretending to suspect origin of rod and holding it in his hand)*: Tell me – where did you . . . *(our inflection for 'where did you' can imply not only that rod was mass produced, but stamped out of synthetic wood.)*

NEW ROD: Well – you know – 'Jackie' Bampton happens to be rather a friend of mine. And my difficulty is that I'm not really comfy unless the action is, well, inches nearer the butt than normal—

OLD ROD *(out-gambited but fighting back)*: Don't worry . . . don't worry . . . it's like a woman. You get used to it. In a couple of years, anyhow, it will be part of you. Even if you don't catch any trout.

If New Rod's rod is longer, with a longer line, and if the river needs such a rod, Old Rod will be in difficulty. Spandrel's Underthwart can be used here.

SPANDREL *(old rodding)*: Nice rod, but it isn't alive till you're about fifteen yards out. I like to throw a shorter line myself.

With right inflection, O.R. can suggest that he is an ancient, almost neolithic, virtuoso of the trout-stream, a sort of Red Indian, really, belly to the ground, who finds no difficulty in trout work at ten yards.[1]

Troutmanship Basic

After practice in the two-approach system with rods, students may then start practising troutmanship proper.

This, too, is essentially an A *vs.* B situation. A the purist, the scholar of dry fly, *vs.* B the rough and ready, the ham, the hack.

Tell my frankly, says A the purist, *were you fishing the water or the rise?*

To counter this accusation of just chucking about, the student trained in Old Rodship should have no difficulty. I'm bound to say that Gattling-Fenn was at his best in this situation. Shirt open to the waist and apparently nut-brown to the navel (actually he wore a 'Suntan Gypsyvest'), Gattling was able to imply 'for Heaven's sake.'

'For Heaven's sake,' he said, and the gleam of his almost suspiciously white teeth suggested 'I'm just a hobo, son – a tramp. My father, and his father before him,[2] were born natural hunters to a man, like every Englishman born a mother's son.'

---

[1] Rodmanship Advance. This year has seen New Rod placed in the one down position by Newer Rod Still. This instrument is made of molecularly reconstituted toilet soap. And though it is associated with wrong-clothesmanship (jacket and trousers clean, and matching) and wrong gadgetmanship (fly-boxes made of perspex) the thing works. We are struggling with this embryonic counter:

NEWER ROD STILL: Yes, it's the first time these fish on the far side of the bend have had a fly decently presented to them.

COUNTERER: Well, I'm bound to admit it makes fishing easier.

N.R.S.: It certainly does.

COUNTERER: I mean, you *could* use a Mills bomb, I suppose.

[2] This would be Gattling-Fenn's grandfather.

While suggesting every word of this, Gattling was at the same time able actually to say:

'I had him in a corner – and – yes, I'm bound to say the fly was a bit damp! Spam Special. Yes, I had to rob the sandwich. . . .'

The following Hargreaves Hampers are worth study, and are useful to others besides troutmen.

1. Do not cast in presence of other fishermen. Proved odds are 93 to 1 against anything happening. So if A says: 'Have a go at him,' you, B, should reply either: 'No – you. I had a good day yesterday,' *or*: 'Oh, that one? He's nearly had me once already. Ruddy great chub.'

2. For use against man who catches fish bigger than yours in same water.

TROUTMAN: That's a good one. What does it weigh?

LAYMAN (*cool*): I don't carry scales.

TROUTMAN: I'll weigh it for you . . . 1¾ pounds. That's funny. How long is it?

LAYMAN: Frankly, I don't carry a tape measure either.

TROUTMAN: I do. . . . Thought so. Nearly 16 inches. That's the trouble with this water, it won't stand fish this size. Ought to be two pounds. It's gone back.

Layman begins to realise he has caught a fish almost on its knees and practically fainting for want of food. He could have picked it out of the water with his bare hands.

3. Rub it in. If, for instance, rival makes clumsy cast, go on and on pointing it out. Thus:

TROUTMAN (*smiling through clenched teeth*): *Now* you've put him down. Now you *have* put him down. Crikey, were you trying to brain him? Doubt if he'll put his nose up for a week. Should think he'd rather drown. I'll move upstream a bit, I think. Happens to all of us.

Marshall's Mangler

This subject is still very 'young' as we call it at Yeovil – i.e. there is still a lot of loose fishing play within our orbit, and a dozen gambits not yet properly described. That is why I am glad to mention Marshall's 'Mangler' – a gambit invented by H. Marshall and needing a finesse and urbanity of execution which totally belie its sobriquet.

The general object is to express an enormous Upper Sixthism so devastating that practically no one else can ever speak about fishing again; and it is done in this way.

The catching of your specific fish is *a Problem*, and must be so approached, without fervour, without even enjoyment.

On one side of your equation is your possible fly, x: on the other, certain variables.

Let α = weather forecast.

γ = weather.

γ^i = flow of stream in relation to mean number of solid factory deposits and old cans.

β = probable age of trout.

o = probable age of fisherman.

π = distance of nearest active motor-bicycle or farm tractor.

δ = temperature of fish.

Then, by a simple calculation jotted down in a waterproof tent with unrunnable ink on unsmudgeable paper, Marshall would get some such equation as this:

$$x = \frac{\delta^{16} o \ \sqrt{\alpha^3 \gamma} \ \ \gamma^i - 8}{\beta^2 \ \pi} = \quad \begin{array}{l} \text{Split's Indefatigable } or \\ \text{Aunt Mary's Special} \end{array}$$

Hand this result with your rod to the ghillie and walk quite slowly away, leaving him to catch the actual fish. Marshall has learnt to intensify the effect of all this by turning up on the bank in a bowler hat and a dark pin-stripe and a pair of thin, blindingly well-polished black shoes, in which he delicately picks his way back through pool and undergrowth.

[178]

17

GONE FISHING

by Keith Waterhouse

KEITH WATERHOUSE is arguably Britain's most popular columnist, mixing as he does ironic comments about our present day society with a layering of good humour directed at human foibles. But apart from his work for *The Daily Mail* and *Punch*, Keith is also a prolific novelist, screen and stage writer, and co-author with Willis Hall of various TV productions including the adventures of the scarecrow, Worzel Gummidge.

Keith's eye for humour has enabled him to win a wide readership of all ages, and though he is no sportsman himself, he can always be relied upon to be pungent and witty when writing about sport. Fishing with its varying images of being the pursuit of rich co-operatives using exclusive stretches of water or else local angling clubs clinging to the banks of a stream constantly threatened with pollution, has long fascinated him. Indeed, he has aired his views on just such matters in some of his books, a number of articles, and perhaps most notably in the following story, 'Gone Fishing' which he wrote for *Punch* in June 1986. Any reader who has belonged to an angling club fighting for survival – not to mention a little space on a river bank – will doubtless allow himself a chuckle or two over the pages which follow . . .

GONE FISHING

As Hon. Secy of the Clogthorpe Angling Socy (affiliated) I have been asked by Herbert to furnish the committee with a verbatim explanation of how the socy came to get unfavourable writeup in chap xi of the library book *Clogthorpe: The Problem of Leisure in an Urban Community* by Geo. Sneap.

First and foremost, let me say straight off that in my personal opinion we came out of it better than the Cemetery Street pitch and toss school, chap viii refers, also that even if Geo. Sneap makes us out to be a bunch of silly b————s, he does not tar us with the same brush as he classes the bellringers, who he implies in so many words that they want their heads tested. See Appendix F: *A culture in decline*.

Geo. Sneap accompanied us in an observatory capacity to the Pride of Yorkshire Silver Shield chub contest (best weight) at Knaresborough on August Bank Holiday Saturday last. How Geo. Sneap came to be chucked into the River Nidd has already been explained in the so-called press report, THREW SOCIOLOGIST IN RIVER ALLEGATION, attached cutting from *Clogthorpe Mercury* refers. My brief is to satisfy the committee how Geo. Sneap came to describe angling as a dying sport when one-nought-seven (107) members and affiliated members definitely set off.

First and foremost, embussing. I spoke to Herbert verbally three times – once on the bowling green, once over a game of fives-and-threes at the Paternosters Arms, and once in the gents' urinal of the Buff's Lodge – and definitely made representations to him that we should not embus outside the Corn Exchange on the same day as they were holding the Cage Birds Show on above premises. Herbert promised to expedite this explosive situation but did not. Result: we are all sitting in the coach, waiting for L. Hetherington (capt) to finish exercising his whippet, when suddenly Thos Longhurst (social secy) asks Geo. Sneap if he has ever seen a black canary. Upon Geo. Sneap opining that he has not, and some of the lads laying bets that it has been dyed, twenty-eight (28) members and affiliated members troop out of the coach and into the Cage Birds Show. We waited half an hour, and only Thos Longhurst (social secy), Geo. Sneap and B. Liversedge (president-elect) returned to the coach, the other lads having joined a queue for cheap budgie seed. See favourable write-up on pets in chap iv.

B. Refreshment stop. First and foremost we should never have stopped at the Terminus Inn, because you as a committee know full well what L. Hetherington (capt) is like when he has got a few inside him. We should have stopped at the Miners' Rest where L. Hetherington (capt) is barred for hitting that woman and would have had to wait in the coach. (Cutting glued in minute book, STRUCK WOMAN WHO TROD ON WHIPPET STORY, refers.) However, this was not implemented

[181]

and we stopped at the Terminus. Result: I as hon secy am sitting in the snug with Geo. Sneap, trying to get a free mention in his book of Herbert's trout (5¾ lb, caught on R. Wharfe, 5/4/67) when in comes L. Hetherington (capt) and bets some of the lads that they cannot race to the top of Terminus Steet and back before the pub clock has finished striking twelve. Eighteen (18) members and affiliated members took L. Hetherington (capt) up on this bet, and out of these, thirteen (13) plus three bystanders including B. Liversedge (president-elect) were arrested in the arguments that followed. Attached cutting, ANGLERS BROKE GLASS IN PUB FRACAS JPS TOLD, refers.

So far, so good. We still had sixty-five (65) members and affiliated members (not bad compared to fiasco on Blackwater Reservoir last Easter – see Appendix A of library book: *Drinking Patterns: A Tentative Analysis*. Blame this on blabmouth Thos Longhurst (social secy), one sniff of barmaid's apron and everything comes out). Of these stalwart members, forty-three (43) definitely clocked in at the River Nidd, not two (2) as stated by Geo. Sneap, *Clogthorpe: The Problem of Leisure in an Urban Community*, p. 142. First and foremost, why as a so-called sociologist didn't he bother to go round the back of the Nidd Arms, where he would have seen eighteen (18) of the lads getting up a cock-fight, also private room of Fisherman's Rest (usual wrestling – six of the lads accounted for). This I admit leaves a discrepancy of thirty-nine (39) lads between what left the Terminus Inn. P. 189 of Geo. Sneap's library book refers:

'One of the few genuinely working-class interests not corroded by television and the bingo hall is the game of nipsy, a primitive kind of golf played with a wooden peg instead of a ball. As many as fifty miners might take part in a nipsy school – possibly because of the opportunities it presents for heavy gambling.'

Geo. Sneap does not give credit where it is due, because

thirty-nine (39) out of that nipsy school were definitely members of the Clogthorpe Angling Socy (affiliated). They joined in above school when we had to de-bus at the York Road toilet facilities at Herbert's request. We always expect to lose a few of the lads to the nipsy school, but this was an unusually high number due to the presence at said event of a team from *World in Action*. Attached cutting, BROKE TV CAMERA IN SCUFFLE SAY POLICE, refers.

3. Choice of judge for fishing match. I have made representations to Herbert on several occasions, both in the urinal of the Buff's Lodge and in a private capacity, to the effect that D. Patterson (judge) does not know a chub from a tin of salmon. As Herbert has personally crossed swords with D. Patterson (judge) in re that disputed bream on Shoddy Mill Ponds last summer (see cutting framed in darts room: BEST FRIEND TRIED TO DROWN ME CLAIMS ANGLER), he cannot blame me for words being exchanged on River Nidd and spoiling a good day's fishing. I definitely did not shove Geo. Sneap in R. Nidd, as wrongly stated in Clogthorpe Magistrates' Court. I shoved D. Patterson (judge) in R. Nidd. D. Patterson (judge) grabbed hold of Herbert, Herbert grabbed hold of me in my capacity as hon secy, and I grabbed hold of Geo. Sneap. I definitely did apologise and pointed out it was his own fault for sticking his nose in and should get back to London with the other pansy-boys.

In conclusion, please excuse pencil as am using the filler of my fountain pen as float for glass-fibre fixed-reel rod. Am getting good results with this and suggest suitable write-up in *Angling Times* to counterbalance unfavourable publicity from Geo. Sneap.

18

THE LORD OF THE FLOWING WATERS

by George Melly

As the man partly responsible for inspiring this collection, it seems only right that George Melly should have the last word on the fun to be found in fishing. Well-known as a jazz singer, George has been a lover of angling ever since he caught his first trout in 1934 when he was just eight years old. Since that day he has taken every opportunity to escape from the pressures of his entertainer's life playing night clubs and concert halls and head for the banks of the River Usk in Wales, where he actually owns the fishing rights to a stretch of water.

Though he approaches the sport with the utmost seriousness and dedication, the always ebullient George is quick to mention things about it which he knows make others laugh. 'I mean,' he explains, 'away from the water, the angler – bewadered, tweed-capped and shapelessly protected against the elements – may present a ludicrous spectacle. But *in situ*, like the penguin, he is perfectly adapted to his environment!'

George Melly writes about fishing with the same mixture of humour and insight, and in this last contribution which he has subtitled, 'Fishing for fun after jazz', tells the story of the lovers' pool that became an angler's pool so that one man could fish happily ever after . . .

THE LORD OF THE FLOWING WATERS

Sometimes, when I am being interviewed in a dressing-room, a glass of wine in hand, a cigarette smouldering in one corner of my mouth, a wide-brimmed stetson on my head, a double-breasted red-check suit hugging my ample frame, with every button doing its work, a journalist asks me what I do to relax. My answer is trout fishing. His response, whether open or politely masked, is incredulity, although actually it is a perfectly rational choice.

What could be more of a contrast to pounding the motorways, the anonymous hotel rooms, the nightly confrontation with an audience in a theatre or smoky night-club than the solitary pleasures of the river bank? Fishing is an

[186]

addiction as demanding as drink if, happily, less damaging to the health. There are two places I would choose to die; in the wings with the applause ringing in my ears; or at the moment of landing a huge trout.

Louis Armstrong, asked to define jazz, said: 'Lady, if you've got to ask, you'll never know.' The same is true in relation to a passion for fishing. I have learnt over the years that to try to explain the fascination is a sure way to empty a room.

Only twice in my life have I made a convert from scratch. The first was a rock drummer from California whom I rather condescendingly showed how to cast and who, within five minutes, had grassed a three-pound brownie and never looked back. The other, a *Guardian* journalist who heard me talk about fishing on the radio, thought he would try it and later admitted in print to being hooked. Both, however, must have been potential anglers waiting for the right stimulus.

Fishing is a true freemasonry. I have met people whom I would normally consider to be crashing bores but who instantly become fascinating on revealing an interest in the Spey roll. I may disagree with someone on every other level – political, social, moral, religious – but as long as his conception of bliss is to approach the water on a likely day I have no quarrel with him.

I do not consider myself a good fisherman. I can cast a long and fairly straight line, but I strike badly, and the trout has really to want to get hooked. This is particularly true when I am on the dry fly. I always used to fish wet partly because, having grown up in the north of England, it was more customary, but mostly because my father did.

He thought dry fly 'sissy' and dismissed the chalk streams as effete, although he had never to my knowledge fished them. 'They don't wade,' he told me. 'They mow the banks and there are little benches to sit on every ten feet.' In a sense he was right but, whereas fishing wet you strike immediately, on the dry fly there is that tiny pause, which has to be exactly timed. Sometimes I manage it. More often I do not. But, as Louis

Armstrong said to the Pope when asked if he and his wife had any children, 'No Pope, but we have lots of fun trying.'

I am also not good about flies. My devotion to the Black Butcher and to the Greenwell Glory is largely because I can recognise them instantly. I know the various sedges, the March Brown and the mayfly, but I am terribly set in my ways. My father was to blame here, too. When asked what to tie on he would advise, 'Anything drab, brownish; try that one'.

So why do I not study the subject if I am that keen? I feel, quite wrongly I know, that to approach fishing over-scientifically is to de-mystify its appeal. I have read and agree with that rather depressing old saw, 'Ten per cent of the fishermen catch 90 per cent of the fish'. I know, too, that I will always be one of the 90 per cent. Even so I realise I will never get down to it. It is as though catching a fish against the odds is, for me, more satisfactory.

I can be lucky. I was once invited, all expenses paid, to Scotland to fish for salmon, something I had never done before. I had this terribly rude old ghillie. 'What do you do for a living?' he asked, staring contemptuously at my thigh waders. I explained I was a journalist (at that time I had temporarily given up singing). 'And can ye afforrrd tae fish here?' he pressed. I admitted to being a guest. 'Aye, I reckoned that,' he said. Nevertheless that weekend I killed two salmon and a big sea trout; the captains of industry and hanging judges, for all their breast waders and wading poles, killed none. They were not best pleased either.

The Usk, a beautiful Welsh river where I own a mile of bank, had been low all through my August holiday a couple of years ago. Then, on my birthday, it flooded. The next day I was back on the road and, as fly fishing was out of the question, decided to spin for a salmon. Usually the run is not until late September. Because of the flood it was early and I got one. I could not help feeling it was a posthumous birthday present from my father.

I am always grateful and fascinated to fish freshwater rivers,

I have learnt to enjoy the chalk streams and increasingly to appreciate, alas, the little benches. Yet there is nothing quite so satisfactory as fishing your own water.

It cost me dear to do this. For the first year or so I rented a stretch of water. Then the owner died and it was put up for auction. I found myself bidding against several tall men in expensive tweeds yet I had to have it or I would own a house within 100 yards of the river and have nowhere to cast a fly.

The figure rose to absurd heights and mentally I began to sell off an increasing number of much-loved pictures I had collected over the years. At £47,000 I got it. That evening a friend toasted me at dinner. 'To the Lord of the flowing waters,' he proposed. I counter-toasted him, 'To the Lord of the empty walls'. I have never regretted it, however.

Several of the pools and stretches are now named, at my wife's suggestion, after the missing paintings. There is the Picasso pool, the Klee rapids, and *The Lovers' Pool*, that being the title of a picture by Magritte; once mine, now water.

ACKNOWLEDGEMENTS

The Editor is grateful to the following authors, agents and publishers for permission to use copyright stories in this collection: Edward Arnold Ltd for 'The Legacy of Noah's Art' by Harry Graham; William Blackwood Ltd for 'The Poacher' by Neil Munro; The Bodley Head for 'The Everlasting Angler' by Stephen Leacock; The Executors of Roland Pertwee for 'The River God'; A. P. Watt Literary Agency for 'An Unlikely Haul' by Lord Dunsany; Methuen & Co Ltd for 'Fish Royal' by A. P. Herbert; Charles Scribner's Sons Inc for 'Fishing in Baden Perfect' by Ernest Hemingway; Michael Joseph Ltd for 'The Little Fishes' by H. E. Bates; Phoenix House Publishers for 'The One That Nearly Got Away' by Maurice Richardson; Rupert Hart-Davis Ltd for 'Troutmanship' by Stephen Potter; *Punch* Publications Ltd for 'Gone Fishing' by Keith Waterhouse; George Melly and *The Field* for 'The Lord of the Flowing Waters'. While every care has been taken to clear permission for use of the stories in this book, in the case of any accidental infringement, copyright holders are asked to contact the editor in care of the publishers.

ACKNOWLEDGEMENTS

The Editor is grateful to the following authors, agents and publishers for permission to use copyright stories in this collection: Edward Arnold Ltd for 'The Legacy of Noah's Art' by Harry Graham; William Blackwood Ltd for 'The Poacher' by Neil Munro; The Bodley Head for 'The Everlasting Angler' by Stephen Leacock; The Executors of Roland Pertwee for 'The River God'; A. P. Watt Literary Agency for 'An Unlikely Haul' by Lord Dunsany; Methuen & Co Ltd for 'Fish Royal' by A. P. Herbert; Charles Scribner's Sons Inc for 'Fishing in Baden Perfect' by Ernest Hemingway; Michael Joseph Ltd for 'The Little Fishes' by H. E. Bates; Phoenix House Publishers for 'The One That Nearly Got Away' by Maurice Richardson; Rupert Hart-Davis Ltd for 'Troutmanship' by Stephen Potter; *Punch* Publications Ltd for 'Gone Fishing' by Keith Waterhouse; George Melly and *The Field* for 'The Lord of the Flowing Waters'. While every care has been taken to clear permission for use of the stories in this book, in the case of any accidental infringement, copyright holders are asked to contact the editor in care of the publishers.